TWO MUMMIES FROM CHIHUAHUA, MEXICO

To Ann Marie
Thank you for
your interest
in this — in
its early
stages.
Rose

(Hope you
can come to
the San Diego
AAFS!)

Hand of female mummy from Chihuahua, Mexico.
(photograph by Peter Koeleman, courtesy of the San Diego Union).

TWO MUMMIES FROM CHIHUAHUA, MEXICO

A MULTIDISCIPLINARY STUDY

Edited by
Rose A. Tyson and Daniel V. Elerick

Contributions by
Elizabeth S. Dyer Alcauskas
Robert A. Bye, Jr.
Nelly Canedo
Jorge Felipe Cárdenas
Judith Strupp Green
Sara B. Laughlin
Anne Marie Luibel-Hulen
Stephen A. Miller
Donald Pate
Stephanie A. Pinter
Spencer L. Rogers
David D. Thompson
Rose A. Tyson
Barton A. Wright

San Diego Museum Papers No. 19

SAN DIEGO MUSEUM OF MAN

1985

Lithographed in the United States of America
by BookCrafters, Inc., Chelsea, Michigan

ISBN 0-937808-40-7

San Diego Museum of Man
1350 El Prado, Balboa Park
San Diego, California 92101

Cover drawings by Barton A. Wright

To the enduring memory of Raymond M. Gilmore
—a most disciplined multidisciplinarian

CONTENTS

ACKNOWLEDGMENTS

The San Diego Museum of Man wishes to acknowledge the generosity of the *Instituto Nacional de Antropología e Historia* in Mexico City for allowing the examination of the subjects of this study--two mummies from Chihuahua. The Museum of Man also is grateful to the *Instituto* for the opportunity to present the results of the mummy research to the public in a physical anthropology exhibit.

As with any project that requires outside assistance, there are many individuals, institutions, and agencies to whom we are indebted. Throughout the research phase, Dr. F. Joseph Luibel gave his time and energy to guide the medical aspects of the project. Special acknowledgment is made to the late Raymond M. Gilmore, Research Associate of the San Diego Natural History Museum, for his encouragement, enthusiasm, and insight. The Museum of Man extends its gratitude to the following:

Harry Affleck, ColorCraft, San Diego
Lois Boylen, M.D., Orthopedic Hospital, Los Angeles
James Dice, Botany Department, San Diego Natural History Museum
Charles L. Chaney, Spectra Company, San Diego
Duffie Clemons, Botany Department, San Diego Natural History Museum
Norman Crawford, San Diego County Sheriff's Office
Howard Scott Gentry, Desert Botanical Garden, Phoenix, Arizona
Larry Goldberger, M.D., Sharp Cabrillo Hospital, San Diego
Gail Kennedy, Ph.D., University of California, Los Angeles
Geoffrey Levin, Ph.D., Curator of Botany, San Diego Natural History
    Museum
Lois Lippold, Ph.D., San Diego State University
Thomas Machado, Veterans Administration Medical Center, San Diego
Helene McHenry, ColorCraft, San Diego
Charles F. Merbs, Ph.D., Arizona State University, Tempe
Suzi Meza, ColorCraft, San Diego
David Miller, ColorCraft, San Diego
Mary Jane Moore, Ph.D., San Diego State University
Anthony P. O'Connell, Sharp-Rees-Stealy Medical Group, San Diego
Homer D. Peabody, Jr., M.D., Sharp-Rees-Stealy Medical Group,
    San Diego
Amadeo Rea, Ph.D., Curator of Birds and Mammals, San Diego Natural
    History Museum
Donald Resnick, M.D., Veterans Administration Medical Center,
    San Diego
Donald Rippon, Veterans Administration Medical Center, San Diego
Leonard Tobey, ColorCraft, San Diego
Debra Trudell, Veterans Administration Medical Center, San Diego
Donald R. Wall, General Atomic, San Diego
Terri Weifenbach, ColorCraft, San Diego
Terry Willingham, San Diego Zoo

Many Museum of Man staff members and volunteers assisted in the editorial phase of the project. Without their time and energy, this volume would not have been possible.

Daniel V. Elerick, Staff, Co-Editor

Ken Hedges, Staff, Editorial and Graphics Advisor

Laura Bartel, Volunteer, Assistant Editor
Jorge F. Cárdenas, Volunteer, Assistant Editor
Julie Cranston, Volunteer, Assistant Editor
Elizabeth A. Zorick, Volunteer, Assistant Editor

Robin Abell, Staff, Typing
Carol Barsi, Staff, Proofreading
Jane Bentley, Staff, Proofreading
Hilary Chester, Volunteer, Proofreading
Jeri Corbin, Staff, Graphics Assistance
Linda Fisk, Staff, Proofreading
Shaun Garcia, Staff, Proofreading
Diane Hamann, Volunteer, Final Proofreading
Donna Kindig, Staff, Graphics Assistance
Harry LaSalle, Volunteer, Photography
Anita McDaniel, Staff, Graphics Assistance
Lilia Monge, Staff, Proofreading
Joan Peterson, Volunteer, Graphics Assistance
Erika Phibbs, Volunteer, Proofreading
Spencer L. Rogers, Staff, Editorial Advice
Timarie J. Seneca, Volunteer, Maps
Douglas Sharon, Staff, Spanish Proofreading

A warm thanks is due all the authors for their research and their continued enthusiasm for the project, and especially to Barton Wright for his drawings.

Rose A. Tyson
Curator, Physical Anthropology

THE CHIHUAHUA MUMMY RESEARCH PROJECT
AT THE SAN DIEGO MUSEUM OF MAN

Rose A. Tyson

INTRODUCTION: THE LEMON GROVE MUMMIES

The following incident occurred on October 17, 1980, in Lemon Grove, California, a small city near San Diego.

A woman cleaning her garage opened a large cardboard carton and, to her horror, beheld a naked human body curled up in the bottom of the box. Her first thought was that a murder had been committed--the body hidden in her garage. Her first action, after her initial fright, was to telephone the San Diego County Sheriff's Office.

Homicide detectives arrived on the scene, which had suddenly become the focus of neighborhood excitement, and upon examination of the "body" found it to be mummified. A brief search turned up another mummy--the fragmentary remains of a small child. The detectives, believing the mummies to be archaeologically important, took them to the San Diego Museum of Man for safekeeping. Local news media made much of the event, and speculation ran high as to the origin of the "Lemon Grove Mummies." The Sheriff's Office continued working on the case, trying to find the "owner" or "owners" of the mummies.

Meanwhile, the mummies had been placed in the Physical Anthropology Laboratory at the Museum of Man (Figure 1). The mummy of the child was missing the head and much of the left side of the body, but the larger mummy was in excellent condition except for some insect damage and hair loss. Museum staff recognized the research value of the mummies, especially if their origin could be established.

Several days later, the newspapers announced that two men had come forward and admitted their responsibility for the mummies. They had brought them from the state of Chihuahua, Mexico, in the 1960s and, after storing them in various garages in the San Diego area, had finally placed them in the garage in Lemon Grove. The daughter of the household had been a good friend of one of the men and had allowed him to store some "belongings" in her mother's garage.

The Sheriff's Office requested that the men come to the museum and describe their acquisition of the mummies to the curators. The following story was derived from notes taken during that meeting.

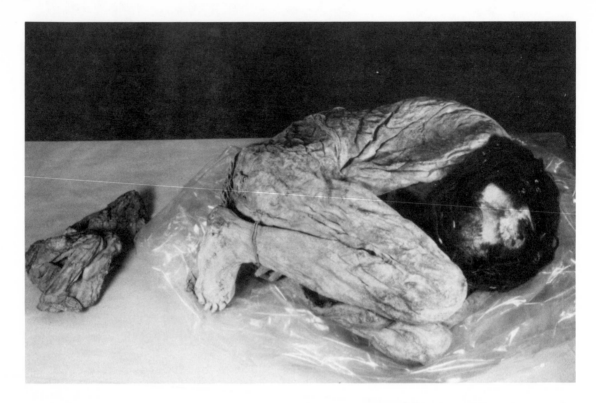

Figure 1. The mummies in the Physical Anthropology Laboratory.

TWO MUMMIES FROM CHIHUAHUA

In October, 1966, two young San Diego men traveled to southwestern Chihuahua, Mexico, in search of prehistoric mummies. The uncle of one of the men knew a Mexican cattle rancher who had heard stories from his cowboys of mummies buried in caves high in the Sierra Madre Occidental. The young men were fascinated by these tales and decided to seek out the caves and their contents for themselves.

Arrangements were made through the ranch owner to have the foreman of his cowboys guide the two *norteamericanos* into the sierras. The foreman was related to the Indians of that area and, despite his 75 years, "ran around like a kid." Several other Indians accompanied them. The party drove to San Bernardo and then continued on horseback into the mountains. The terrain was extremely rugged, and traveling was done mainly in the canyon bottoms and arroyos. The young men dressed warmly but were uncomfortably cold. The Indians, however, were dressed in light clothing and sandals and did not seem the least bit chilled, even though there was snow on the ground.

The small group ate at ranches whenever they could, but otherwise their staple foods were jerky and tortillas. They spent one month in the mountains, looking for caves and exploring them. A team of Canadian archaeologists reportedly was excavating in the area, but the two groups did not come into contact.

About one-third of the caves they visited showed human activity, either as habitation or burial caves, or sometimes both. Exploring these caves was difficult; no trails led up the steep cliff faces, and the rough shale made climbing dangerous. The habitation caves had hearths with fire-altered rocks and broken pottery. Some of the caves had large deposits of bat guano which reached nearly a meter in depth.

The last cave they explored was different. It was large, guano-free, and faced east on a gradual, pine-covered slope with trails leading to the opening. This "hollow in the hill" extended about 9 meters into the mountain. Cattle, as well as wild animals, had used it for shelter. Pottery sherds of reddish clay and light brown clay with black markings were scattered around the perimeter, and the surface was covered with a fine dust from the trampling of cattle.

The fragmentary remains of a child mummy were partially exposed near the edge of the cave. It had been damaged by the cattle. After removing the mummy, the men dug deeper into the cave floor and, at approximately 70 cm from the surface, encountered a mat-wrapped bundle. The mat, though brittle, was in good condition. It was constructed of a broad, flat fiber which they thought was palm, although they had not seen any palm trees in the vicinity. The ends of the mat were folded inside "like an egg roll" and then sewn shut with a vine or fiber cord. Unwrapping the bundle, they found the tightly flexed body of a mummified female. Food offerings had been placed in the cavity formed by the limbs and the torso--an ear of corn, about 15 cm in length, with small yellow kernels; some date-like objects about 2.5 cm in length with a shiny, amber coat and a stem scar on one end; an animal bone, about 10 cm long, with dried meat still attached; and some dark-colored berries.

The body was in excellent condition with the hair and skin intact. The burial pit was about a meter across and was lined with large pieces of pine bark about 3 cm thick. Although the bark showed evidence of fire, its surface immediately surrounding the mummy was not charred. Below the mummy was another layer of bark, then a layer of dirt. Below this was another mummy. There were other mummies in the cave, seemingly placed in layers.

With their objective accomplished, the two men decided to take the two mummies with them. On their trip out of the mountains, the horse of one of the men fell and crushed its rider's leg, making further travel impossible. A message was sent to a nearby ranch, and after much delay, a small plane landed on the mesa above them. A harrowing takeoff from the mesa top nearly finished the trip for the injured man, the pilot, and the two mummies. The plane was overloaded, and the short takeoff area required that the guides and the remaining American hold the wings until the engine reached maximum rpm. Then, with a wildly jolting take-off, the plane lunged over the mesa's edge in a dive--the stall-warning horn blaring until flying speed was reached.

Eventually, the mummies and the two young men rejoined. At first they planned to take the mummies to a museum, but one young man was immediately drafted and sent to Vietnam. The mummies instead were stored in three different garages over the next 14 years until a Lemon Grove resident rediscovered them.

MUSEUM RESEARCH PROJECT

The two men (they were in their late teens when they took the mummies) pointed out the approximate location on a map, lat. 27° 40' N and long. 108° 36' W (Figure 2). Their description of the mummy burial is consistent with reports by Zingg (1940) and Ascher and Clune (1960) for the archaeology of the area. Zingg (1940:7) excavated a burial cist lined with large slabs of pine bark, the entire cist capped with white mud, and Ascher and Clune (1960:271) excavated ears of corn and numerous acorns in association with mat-wrapped mummies at Waterfall Cave in southern Chihuahua. The date-like objects described by the two men were probably acorns. Unfortunately, all the food offerings and the mat were lost during storage.

With the origin of the mummies established, the first consideration was status of ownership. The discoverers wanted to give the mummies to the Museum of Man but were informed the mummies belonged to Mexico and could not be donated.

Meanwhile, plans were forming for a major physical anthropology exhibit, at the Museum of Man, which would explore the interactions of culture, environment, and genetics and show how these interactions influence the human body. The exhibit--"Bodies and Bones: The Inside Story"--was to open the following year. Specimens from the Hrdlička paleopathology collection (Tyson and Alcauskas 1980) and the Stanford-Meyer osteopathology collection (acquired in May, 1981) were to form the nucleus of the exhibition specimens. An important part of the exhibit would be devoted to mummy research and would illustrate what can be learned of ancient health and disease from mummified remains. Peruvian mummies from the museum's collections and Egyptian mummies from the Los Angeles County Museum of Natural History were to be featured in the display.

With the arrival of the Chihuahuan mummies, a unique opportunity for research and exhibition was presented. Arrangements were made with the *Instituto Nacional de Antropología e Historia* in Mexico City to retain the mummies for this purpose. It was understood from the beginning of the project that research would not include autopsy. Non-destructive techniques such as radiography and computer assisted tomography, supplemented by small-scale tissue sampling, could provide a modest but significant amount of data.

With only one year to accomplish the research and prepare it for presentation to the public, a great deal of help was needed from outside the museum, especially from researchers, medical institutions, and volunteers. By its nature, the project required a multidisciplinary approach. Various aspects such as description, CAT scanning, botanical identification, cause of death, hair/protein study, and ethnographic analysis were undertaken by researchers associated with the museum and by graduate students from San Diego State University. F. Joseph Luibel, M.D. (Figure 3), pathologist at Sharp Cabrillo Hospital, designed the medical aspects of the research, and this author coordinated the project.

Radiocarbon dating was one of the first considerations. The female mummy was dated at 860 ± 40 years before present (LJ 5301), calibrated

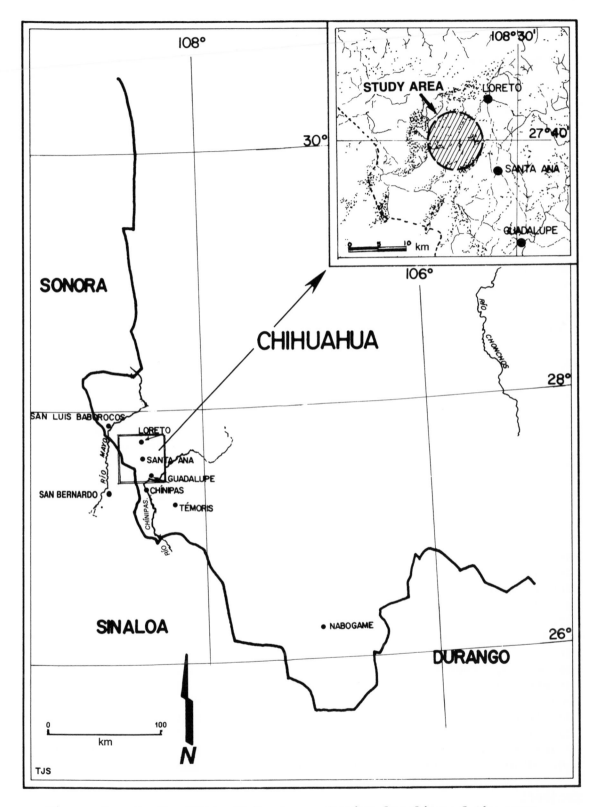

Figure 2. Southwestern Chihuahua, showing locality of the cave
(after Pennington 1963:Map 1).

to A.D. 1040-1260 (Timothy Linick, personal communication, 1982). A sample of fifteen grams of cordage from the mummy's string apron-skirt was used to obtain the date.

Results were presented March 21, 1981, at the Annual Meeting of the Southwestern Anthropological Association in Santa Barbara, California, in a symposium entitled: "Preliminary Studies of Two Mummies from Chihuahua, Mexico." It was co-chaired by Barton A. Wright, then Scientific Director of the Museum of Man, and by this author. Papers were presented by Alcauskas, Canedo, Green, Luibel-Hulen, Miller, Pinter, Rogers, Wright, and Tyson; the published versions of these papers are included in this volume.

Research continued on the project and an update--"Two Mummies from Chihuahua, Mexico"--was given for the public as part of a lecture series augmenting the opening of the "Bodies and Bones" exhibit. On November 13, 1981, the exhibit opened with a large section devoted to the Chihuahuan mummy research project (Figure 4). Photographs, radiographs, CAT scans, scanning electron microscopy, drawings, and explanatory materials were displayed with the female mummy. The fragmentary mummy of the child was not displayed. By the time the exhibit closed on June 12, 1983, over 300,000 people had visited the exhibit.

Further updates have been given (Tyson 1982a,b). To the original 9 papers, 5 have been added for this volume: Pate, Thompson and Laughlin, Bye (2 papers), and Cárdenas. Future studies are planned to cover subjects such as entomology, histology by means of an endoscope, histochemistry, 3-dimensional scans (using a Cemax 1000 3-Dimensional Scanner), and dating of the child mummy.

CONCLUSIONS

The rationale behind this study was to provide biocultural data from which to infer circumstances of health and disease, and their attendant cultural components, of two members of an ancient culture. Introductory papers (Tyson and Wright) are followed by biological studies based on the mummies (Pinter, Pate, Luibel-Hulen, Thompson and Laughlin, Canedo, and Alcauskas). The botanical identifications by Miller provide a transition to cultural and environmental studies by Rogers, Bye, and Green. The final paper, in Spanish, is a summary by Cárdenas.

A mummy has been likened to a time capsule, brought to the present from a past age. What that capsule contains is not only a record of a single life, but also information on the biological and cultural environment of which it was an integral part. How much of this information we are able to interpret is dependent upon our expertise and the lengths to which we are willing to go before destroying the very container of this information. A balance must be struck between the search for information and the willingness to leave some parts of the record for a later time--to pass the capsule on to another generation.

Figure 3. Dr. Luibel examining the female mummy.

Figure 4. The Chihuahuan mummy exhibit.

REFERENCES CITED

Ascher, Robert, and Francis J. Clune, Jr.
    1960   Waterfall Cave, Southern Chihuahua, Mexico. American
           Antiquity 26(2):270-274.

Tyson, Rose A.
    1982a A Female Mummy from Chihuahua, Mexico. Poster presentation,
           Annual Meeting of the American Association of Physical
           Anthropologists, Eugene, Oregon, April 1-3, 1982.

    1982b Multidisciplinary Research on a Female Mummy, Dated 830 $\pm$ 60
           Years B.P., from Chihuahua, Mexico. Paper presented at the
           44th International Congress of Americanists, Manchester,
           England, September 5-9, 1982.

Tyson, Rose A., and Elizabeth S. Dyer Alcauskas, eds.
    1980   Catalogue of the Hrdlička Paleopathology Collection.
           Descriptions by Charles F. Merbs. Photographs by Nancy
           Christensen. Forward and Glossary by Spencer L. Rogers.
           San Diego: San Diego Museum of Man.

Zingg, Robert M.
    1940   Report on Archaeology of Southern Chihuahua. Contributions
           of the University of Denver, Center of Latin American
           Studies, No. 1. Denver, Colorado: The University of Denver.

COMMENTS ON MUMMIFICATION
IN THE AMERICAN SOUTHWEST

Barton A. Wright

Scattered about the world are regions wherein the climatic conditions are such that the bodies of the deceased inhabitants are subjected to desiccation so rapid that the natural processes of decay and disintegration do not occur, resulting in a dehydrated body or mummy. In Egypt, and to some extent Peru, this natural phenomenon was enhanced over the span of five or six millennia by the development of cultural practices designed to ensure more consistent results in preserving the human body. These procedures were supported by religious or philosophical concepts which promoted the belief that preserving the bodies of important individuals allowed the living to derive some good from their continued presence in either the natural or supernatural world.

The American Southwest is one of the regions where desiccation can occur with sufficient rapidity to produce a mummified body. In this area, climatic conditions capable of maintaining the necessary aridity have remained relatively unchanged for the past seven or eight millennia. This has been delineated by increasingly accurate climatological studies as well as by an occasional paleontological discovery. These arid conditions prevailed throughout a region which reaches from Canada deep into Mexico and spans the entire Intermontane West. Within this space, countless habitational sites, many in protected locations, have produced archaeological data indicating that the area has been occupied for at least 10,000 years. Where these prehistoric people lived they often buried their dead, and the bodies should have survived with ease. Yet, despite the fact that all of the requisites are present for mummification to occur, the actual number of preserved bodies is relatively small. In a land area of over two million square kilometers only a few hundred mummies have been recovered. This is in great contrast to Egypt, where a land area less than one-hundredth as large produced mummies in such quantity that they have been used as fuel for steam engines and exported for pharmaceutical supplies for centuries. This rarity of mummies may be due in part to the practice of cremation throughout a large segment of the area where mummification would most easily have occurred. It appears more likely, however, that conditions were not as favorable for the preservation of bodies as existed in Egypt and Peru, or that the population was sparse. Possibly both were factors.

An examination of the literature reveals several interesting items of information concerning mummies. Most are derived from Utah and Arizona with lesser numbers occurring in Colorado, New Mexico, and northern Mexico. Occasionally, mummies have been found in outlying areas such as

Texas and Nevada. The area which has produced the majority of mummies in the Southwest is the canyon and mesa land of the Four Corners of Arizona, New Mexico, Colorado, and Utah. Interestingly, this is the area where the sterile sands of Navajo sandstone occur, a sand which is virtually indistinguishable in its characteristics from the Nubian sand of Egypt from which the mummies of the average inhabitants have been removed.

Most of the mummies recovered in the Southwest were buried in a relatively short period lasting from A.D. 100 to 1300. Within this 1,200 year span are two peak periods, one occurring early, about A.D. 500 to 700, and the other much later, about A.D. 1100 to 1200. This poses an interesting question. If conditions were favorable and humans were present, and at least half of them did not practice cremation, why are there not more preserved bodies? More specifically, what has happened to the deceased from the first five or six millennia?

The relatively small number of Southwestern mummies makes them an invaluable but finite resource. It is a resource limited not only by the rarity with which desiccation of a human body takes place, but also by the changing ethics and ethnic attitudes of today.

In the Southwest, the use of the term "mummification practices" (El-Najjar and Mulinski 1980:103) is somewhat misleading. There was no "practice" of mummification, but rather a natural accident due to the choice of a protected burial location without any cultural process such as embalming to enhance preservation (El-Najjar and Mulinski 1980:103). The characteristics of the soil, grave preparation, and cerements all aided a rapid, natural dehydration. The physical properties of the soil may well have more to do with the process of desiccation than has been previously acknowledged. Certainly the preservation in Navajo sandstone and the salt-laden soils of the Sierra Madre of Mexico would indicate this. Grave preparation, which is remarkably uniform throughout the area, may assist this natural process. In most instances, preparations consisted of a pad of grass or fiber upon which the body was placed and covered or wrapped with a mat, twined bag, or basket. Within this outer covering the body was often dressed in a fur or feather blanket. These preparations allowed the movement of air through the interstices. Possibly each was a factor in the drying process, but little research has been conducted into this aspect.

The selection of burial sites in locations favorable to preservation has added immeasurably to our knowledge of the perishable parts of the earlier inhabitants' material culture--derived mainly from the grave offerings included with the bodies. Analysis of this material has produced inferences, some highly subjective, regarding the beliefs and philosophies of these people. The same degree of attention, however, has not been directed toward the human remains until recently. In the past, there was a tendency to treat the mummified remains as an artifact or specimen to be displayed for public viewing, rather than as a source of information about unwritten history. This attitude has undergone great change in the past two decades. In part, this is due to new developments in medical science offering avenues of research not formerly available. It also occurred because of the objection of various Native American groups to having the bodies of their antecedents placed on public view. The demand for respect of the dead has led to the removal of mummies from museum displays across the country; most have been placed in laboratories, where attention has been focused on the possibilities they offer for research.

Examples of this increase in mummy research are described in El-Najjar and Mulinski (1980:103). Four mummies from Canyon de Chelly in northern Arizona have been studied at Case Western Reserve University in Cleveland, Ohio. A partial mummy was examined at the Human Variation Laboratory, Arizona State University, Tempe, and the desiccated body of a Pueblo child was investigated at the Department of Anthropology in this same university.

A complete autopsy will destroy the integrity of the mummy for future examinations, although presumably, later histological studies can be conducted if the remaining tissue is kept under humidity control. Studies by El-Najjar and others indicate the necessity of maintaining mummy tissue in desiccated condition if studies of proteins and enzymes are to be carried out in the future, as there is complete degeneration in six months once the tissue has been rehydrated. This information was derived from work on an adult and an infant from Canyon de Chelly (El-Najjar et al. 1980:197-202).

It might be useful at this point to evaluate the number of mummies available for study. El-Najjar and Mulinski (1980:103-117) list only 43 specimens from Arizona, New Mexico, and Texas. The parameters of this survey are not clearly stated, and certainly, in addition to those listed, there are an equal number of mummified bodies from such places as White Dog Cave, Tseahtso, Tsegi, Tularosa, Broken Roof Cave, and many others. To these formally excavated areas there should be added the pot-hunted, accidental finds throughout the Southwest. A brief survey of the literature indicates that another 50 mummies have been excavated and still another 10 have come from accidental finds. There are several areas such as Utah and Mexico where information is sparse; nevertheless, the information is sufficient to indicate that an estimated number of mummies would fall between one and two hundred and would undoubtedly be on the low end of this range. Of this total, few mummies are complete. Most are only partially mummified, while a few other specimens consist of body parts, such as the mummified scalp of an entire head or a pair of forearms and hands. Occasionally, a burial has been termed a mummy even if it retains only a few ligaments or bits of skin. Despite the fact that the survey by El-Najjar and Mulinski is incomplete, the percentages appear to hold true for the estimated number of Southwestern mummies as well. Consequently, it would be reasonable to expect that about 40% of the bodies recovered would be complete. For all mummies recovered in the Southwest, only one-third would be adults; the others would be subadults, with the largest portion being infants. Presumably an adult body should be a more complete compendium of information, having been exposed longer to the "slings and arrows of outrageous fortune." But regardless of whether this latter observation is correct or not, the estimated figures indicate that mummies are in very limited supply. Not only are they few in number, but they are scattered across the country in the ownership of museums, private collections, and even art galleries.

The recent increase in autopsies of Southwestern mummies will render many of these specimens useless for further studies, and interest generated by this activity will reduce the supply at an even greater rate. I firmly believe that a coordination of studies should be attempted which would ensure that as many researchers as possible use this valuable resource before it is decimated by complete autopsies. There are many studies being done at present, but an equal number remain yet to be done. Conservation of such a limited resource should be the first concern of all involved.

REFERENCES CITED

El-Najjar, Mahmoud Y.; Jaime Benitez; Gary Fry; George E. Lynn; Donald J. Ortner; T. A. Reyman; and Parker A. Small
    1980   Autopsies on Two Native American Mummies. American Journal of Physical Anthropology 53(2):197-202.

El-Najjar, Mahmoud Y., and Thomas M. J. Mulinski
    1980   Mummies and Mummification Practices in the Southwestern and Southern United States. In: A. Cockburn and E. Cockburn, eds., Mummies, Disease, and Ancient Cultures, pp. 103-117. Cambridge: Cambridge University Press.

DESCRIPTIONS OF TWO MUMMIES
FROM CHIHUAHUA, MEXICO

Stephanie A. Pinter

INTRODUCTION

The physical anthropologist, accustomed to the examination of dry bone specimens, must adjust to the specialized techniques needed for the study of a mummy, including anatomical observation and comparative radiography (Angel 1980:241). The data collected may resemble a forensic report: sex, age, stature, build, occupation, genetic variations, blood type, race, health, diseases, time elapsed since death, and cause of death. The results of such a study are dependent upon the condition of the mummy, the techniques available, and the extent to which the specimen is sampled or examined by autopsy.

The subjects of this study are a child mummy and an adolescent mummy from southwestern Chihuahua, Mexico. This paper presents physical descriptions of the mummies based on direct observation and examination of radiographs. The child has not yet been dated, but the adolescent mummy has been dated at A.D. 1040-1260 by the radiocarbon method (Tyson, this volume). The mummies were found in an area occupied by the present-day Tarahumara, although in earlier times the Varohio, a related group, also lived in the region (Green, this volume). Considering that the Tarahumara have been in the area for possibly 2,000 years (Pennington 1963: 12), it would be useful to examine related studies for comparative material.

A review of the literature shows very few published studies on the biology of the Tarahumara. Early observations by Hrdlička (1908) and Basauri (1929) reported some anthropometrical and physiological data, and Leche (1933) studied dermatoglyphics and lateral dominance. In the mid 1950s, Echeverria (Matson 1970:Table 1) studied blood types, and Gajdusek and Rogers (1955) analyzed specific serum antibodies. More recently, Rodriguez and others (1963) investigated blood group antigens, Balke and Snow (1965) reported the endurance capabilities of kickball racers, and Snyder and others (1969) examined the penetrance and expressivity of Carabelli's cusp and the protostylid.

DESCRIPTION OF THE CHILD MUMMY

The body of the child mummy (Figure 1) is in a loosely flexed position, with the legs drawn up to the abdomen and the spine straight. The right arm is bent slightly with the hand curving up, resting on the right thigh. There are no fingernails. The body is fragmentary, missing the skull, left scapula, left clavicle, left ribs, the entire left arm, the cervical and thoracic vertebrae, left metatarsals, and the phalanges of both feet.

14

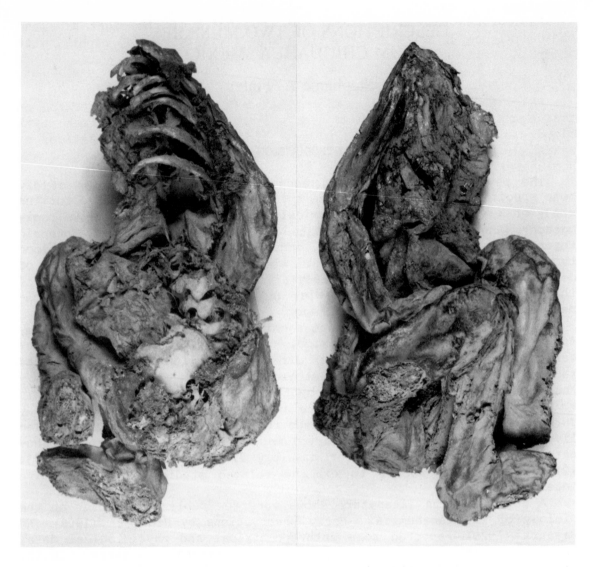

Figure 1. Left and right sides of child mummy.

The skin is dry and hard with large patches missing, either from flaking or from having been chewed by small animals. Skin color ranges from yellow-brown to dark red-brown. Internal organs are missing, but the spinal cord is present. Much of the skin is coated with a layer of gray dirt and dust.

Sex and Age Determination

The determination of sex was made from direct observation of the external genitalia, showing the mummy to be female. Age was estimated from the measurements of three long bones: the femur, 11.75 cm; the tibia, 9.75 cm; and the humerus, 9.0 cm. Using metrical data on long bone growth of infants and children from the Indian Knoll, Kentucky, skeletal population (Johnston 1962:Table 2), the mummy's age at death is estimated between 0.5 and 1.5 years.

Pathology

Radiographs show a thickening of the shafts of the right ulna and radius (Figure 2, left) and the tibia and fibula (Figure 2, right), with attendant periostitis (Alcauskas, this volume).

Blood Type

Pate (this volume) has used the mixed cell agglutination method on tissue to determine the blood type as O. This is in agreement with blood group distributions of the present-day indigenous populations of Mexico, which are characterized mainly as type O (Mourant, Kopeć, and Domaniewska-Sobczak 1958:197).

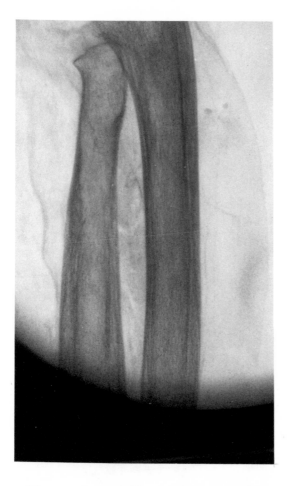 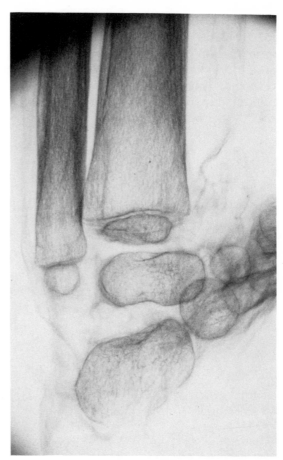

Figure 2. Radiographs showing periostitis on bones of child mummy. Left: ulna and radius. Right: tibia and fibula.

DESCRIPTION OF THE ADOLESCENT MUMMY

The adolescent mummy is in a tightly flexed position with the knees drawn up to the chest. The head is bent forward, and the shoulders are hunched (Figure 3), with the spine curved into a C-shape (Figure 4). The left arm is across the left side of the face; the hands protrude from between the legs (Figure 5). The feet are crossed and are in line with the hips. Areas of skin on the left hip and shoulder show the impression of the mat in which the body was wrapped (Green, this volume). For this reason, and from the flattened mouth and chin area, it is probable the body was placed on the left side. Darkened areas of the skin on the left shoulder may represent dependent post-mortem lividity (Figure 6), further evidence of the burial position.

The mummy is nearly complete, missing only the distal phalanges of the left foot. On the long axis, the body measures 61.2 cm from the tip of the toes to the top of the shoulders; transversely, from the knees to the curved back, it measures 48.1 cm; it is 29.1 cm thick. The weight is 6.25 kg.

The skin is hard and dry with very little resilience and ranges in color from yellow-brown to red-brown. Although the literature cites some cases in which saws were needed to cut the skin of a mummy, in this case, it was possible to use a scalpel to remove skin sections. The skin has numerous small holes from insect damage, a condition that occurred during the mummy's 14 years of garage storage.

Figure 3. Adolescent female mummy.

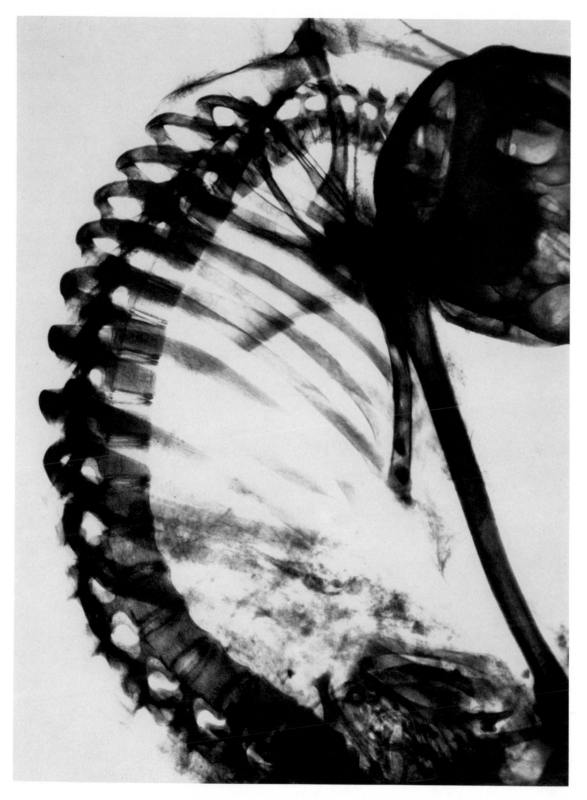

Figure 4. Radiograph of adolescent female mummy.

18

Figure 5. Hands of adolescent female mummy.

Figure 6. Arrows indicate darkened area of probable
dependent post-mortem lividity.

When first found, the black hair was in excellent condition (personal communication from discoverers, 1980), but during storage, hair loss had progressed from the top of the head to the nape of the neck, with hair still in place at the front and sides. A large insect nest is attached to the scalp hair. The length of the hair has not been measured because most of it is twisted as part of the hairstyle. Some of the eyebrows and eyelashes remain. The eyes are open, showing the desiccated eyeballs. The toenails and fingernails (see Frontispiece) are missing, and the outer layer of skin is peeling from the fingers (Figure 7). Bits of dirt and residue are attached to the skin. There is evidence that the mummy had been tied tightly in the flexed position, as indentations in the skin can be seen on the legs (Figure 8). The discoverers, however, deny any ropes being on the mummy when it was unwrapped (personal communication, 1985).

Associated Clothing and Ornamentation

The mummy is wearing a string apron-skirt, plant fiber hairbands, and string anklets (Green, this volume). The left anklet is approximately 18 cm in circumference, indicating a relatively small ankle size. The right earlobe is pierced by a wooden plug (probably the left earlobe is also pierced, but it cannot be seen).

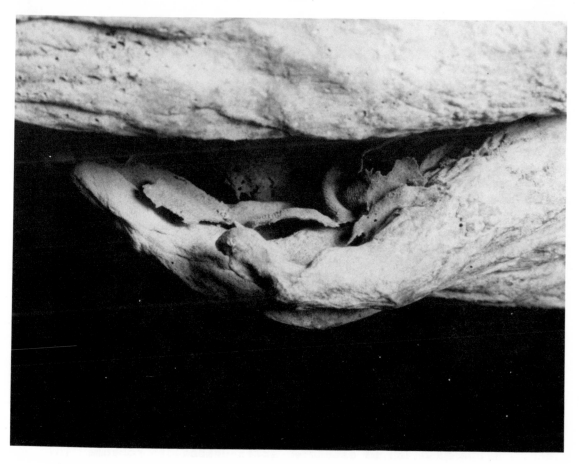

Figure 7. Outer layer of skin peeling from palm and fingers.

Figure 8. Rope impression (arrows) on right leg.

Determination of Sex

From the first observation, the mummy was designated female because of the rather developed breasts. The genital region is hidden by the string apron-skirt and the flexed position. The enlarged abdomen suggested pregnancy. These observations were confirmed by radiographic examination (Figure 9).

Age of the Fetus

The fetus was estimated to have a gestation age of 28-32 weeks. This estimation was made from biparietal measurements using modern growth tables (Luibel-Hulen, this volume; Alcauskas, this volume). The overlapping of the fetal skull bones and their position in the pelvic area suggest that labor had begun (Alcauskas, this volume).

Determination of Age

Radiographs show all permanent teeth in place except the third molars (Figure 10), which are in partial development in the jaw with the crowns already formed and the roots in the process of forming. The lower third molars are angled toward the second molars and probably would have become impacted with further growth. Using Ubelaker's chart (1978:47) for the formation and eruption of teeth among American Indians, the age at death is estimated at 15 years ± 36 months. This age is corroborated by Thompson and Laughlin (this volume).

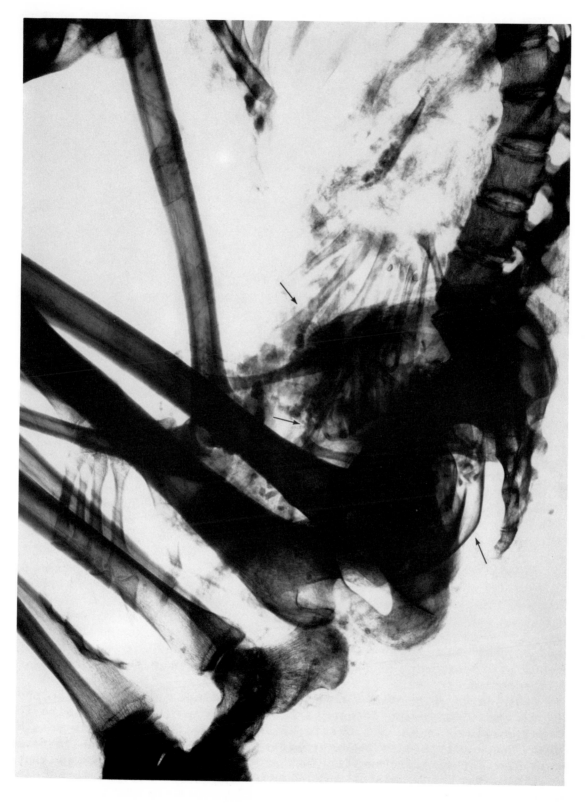

Figure 9. Radiograph showing fetal bones within pelvic area.

22

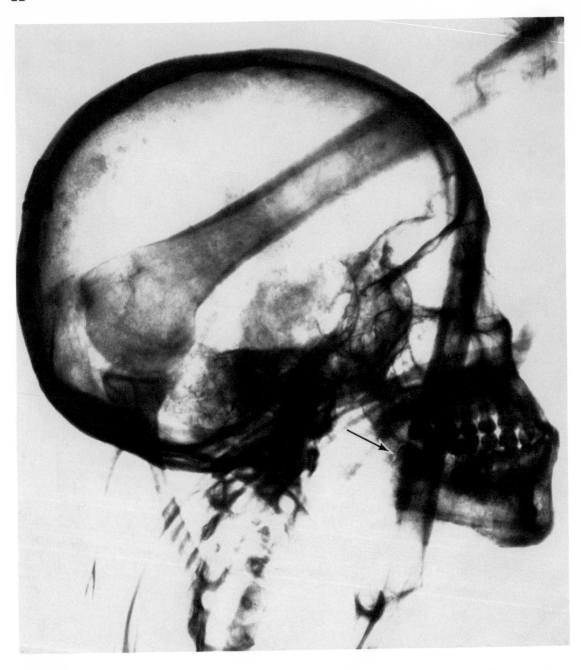

Figure 10. Radiograph of skull. Arrow indicates unerupted third molar.

Other evidence for the age at death is the non-fusion of the epiphysis of the iliac crest (Figure 11) and those of the vertebral bodies (see Figure 4). Time of initial fusion of the iliac crest for females ranges between 17 and 19 years (Ubelaker 1978:53, Table 6), while final fusion of epiphyses of the vertebrae ranges between 17 and 25 years (Bass 1971:78). The distal epiphysis of the tibia has not fused completely. Age of initial union is estimated between 14 and 16 years (Ubelaker 1978:53, Table 6).

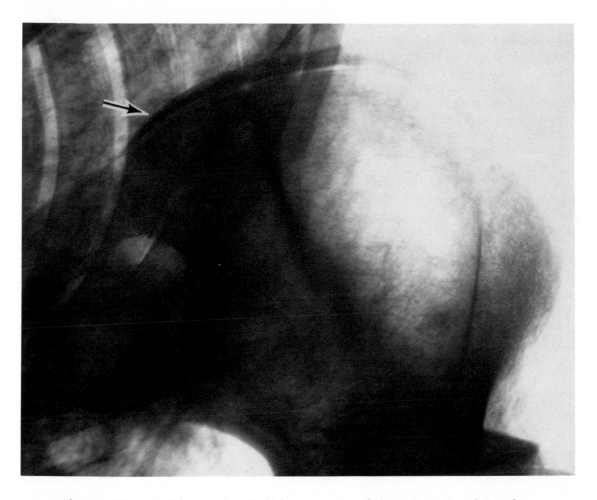

Figure 11. Radiograph of iliac crest with unfused epiphysis.

Stature Estimation

Stature estimation was based on the radiographic measurements of two long bones, using data by Genovés (1967:74-75, Table 13):

Bone	Length (in cm)	Stature (in cm)
Femur	41.5	154.5
Tibia	35.0	156.5

According to Genovés (1967:74), the tibia has the highest correlation with stature; therefore, using the tibial length of 35.0 cm, the estimated stature for this individual is 156.5 cm (5 ft 2 in).

Pathologies

Radiographs of the skull (see Figure 10) show the mandible to be dislocated and projecting forward. Whether this was an ante-mortem trauma or a post-mortem phenomenon is unknown. The mandible may have fallen forward after death because of the face-down position.

A scalp sample (approximately 3.0 x 3.5 cm) was taken from the base
of the head for hair follicle analysis (Canedo, this volume). Viewed
through the resultant opening, the occipital region of the skull showed
a raised porous area offset from the surrounding bone by its darker
color (Figure 12). This porosity may be evidence of a benign bone tumor
or a calcified subperiosteal hematoma. The latter condition can be the
result of trauma or of scurvy--a vitamin C deficiency (Gregg, personal
communication, 1981). Of these possibilities, trauma may be the most
likely, as radiographs show raised and uneven areas at several other locations on the skull (Figure 13).

What may be growth arrest lines show on the medial aspect of the
right distal tibia (Figure 9). Resnick (personal communication, 1985)
could not make a definite identification, as the condition usually occurs bilaterally and symetrically. No abscesses or caries in the dentition were apparent in the radiographs (Figure 10).

Blood Type

A sample of tissue taken from the left ankle region included a blood
vessel (Figure 14) by which Dr. Lois Boylen, Department of Hematology,
Orthopedic Hospital, Los Angeles, determined the tissue to be type O
(see also Pate, this volume). This agrees with present-day blood group
distributions, the indigenous populations of Mexico being characterized
mainly by type O (Mourant, Kopeć, and Domaniewska-Sobczak 1958:197).

Figure 12. Incision in scalp showing porosity of skull surface.

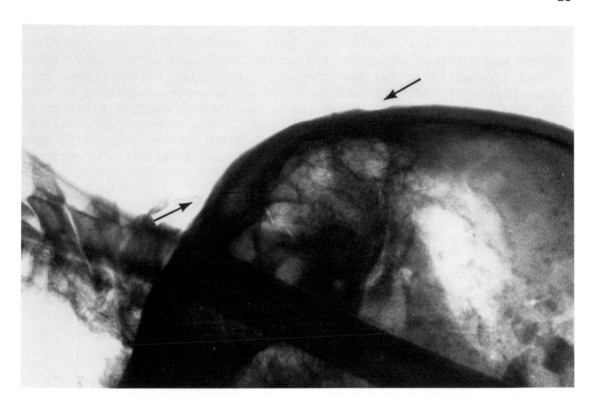

Figure 13. Radiograph of skull showing uneven areas on surface.

Figure 14. Tissue with blood vessel from left ankle
(scale in mm).

DISCUSSION

The two mummies, child and adolescent, represent individuals from an ancient population of northern Mexico. The undated child mummy was a female between 6 and 18 months of age. The pregnant female, A.D. 1040-1260, was approximately 15 years old at the time of death; fetal age was between 28 and 32 weeks.

Body build of the adolescent female was relatively slight with slender hands and feet. The stature estimate of 156.5 cm may be compared to figures obtained for Tarahumara populations by Hrdlička (1908:133; 1935: 269, Table 17) and Basauri (1929:21):

	Sample Size	Average (in cm)	Range (in cm)
Hrdlička	10	150.7	148.6-159.6
Basauri	30	150.0	143.5-154.0

Tissue from both mummies has been typed as O, which corresponds to results of a blood group study by Echeverria on 113 Tarahumaras, among whom admixture was calculated to be 9.96%. These data, reported in Matson (1970:Table 1), are:

Blood Type	Percentage
O	92.92
A	4.92
B	2.67
AB	0.00

The radiographs of the adolescent female mummy's dentition are not sufficiently detailed to show presence or absence of Carabelli's cusp. The present-day Tarahumara have a very high frequency of this trait, which is usually low in Mongoloid populations (Snyder et al. 1969).

This study, although preliminary in nature, has revealed some information on the two Chihuahuan mummies. In time, and with improved techniques of analysis, data from these physical remains will increase.

ACKNOWLEDGMENTS

I would like to thank Dr. John B. Gregg of the University of South Dakota, School of Medicine, for his advice concerning the pathologies of the pregnant female mummy; and Dr. Lois Boylen, Department of Hematology, Orthopedic Hospital, Los Angeles, for her assistance in the blood typing. Much gratitude is extended to Ms. Terry Willingham of the San Diego Zoo Hospital and Dr. Donald Resnick of the Veterans Administration Medical Center, San Diego, for the radiographs. The assistance of J. D. McPike, M.D., G. Salazar, M.D., and J. Champaign, M.D., Department of Radiology, Naval Hospital, San Diego, is greatly appreciated.

REFERENCES CITED

Angel, J. Lawrence
1980   Physical Anthropology: Determining Sex, Age, and Individual
        Features. In: A. Cockburn and E. Cockburn, eds., Mummies,
        Disease, and Ancient Cultures, pp. 241-157. Cambridge:
        Cambridge University Press.

Balke, Bruno, and Clyde Snow
1965   Anthropological and Physiological Observations on Tarahumara
        Endurance Runners. American Journal of Physical
        Anthropology 23(3):293-301.

Basauri, Carlos
1929   Monografía de los Tarahumaras. México, D.F.: Talleres
        Gráficos de la Nación.

Bass, William M.
1971   Human Osteology: A Laboratory and Field Manual of the Human
        Skeleton. Columbia: Missouri Archaeological Society,
        University of Missouri.

Gajdusek, D. C., and N. G. Rogers
1955   Specific Serum Antibodies to Infectious Disease Agents in
        Tarahumara Adolescents of Northwestern Mexico. Pediatrics
        16:819-834.

Genovés, Santiago C.
1967   Proportionality of Long Bones and Their Relation to Stature
        among Mesoamericans. American Journal of Physical
        Anthropology 26(1):67-78.

Hrdlička, Aleš
1908   Physiological and Medical Observations among the Indians
        of Southwestern United States and Northern Mexico. Bureau
        of American Ethnology, Bulletin 34. Washington, D.C.:
        Government Printing Office.

1935   The Pueblos, with Comparative Data on the Bulk of the Tribes
        of the Southwest and Northern Mexico. American Journal of
        Physical Anthropology 20(3):235-460.

Johnston, Francis E.
1962   Growth of the Long Bones of Infants and Young Children at
        Indian Knoll. American Journal of Physical Anthropology
        20(3):249-254.

28

Leche, Stella M.
    1933   Dermatoglyphics and Functional Lateral Dominance in Mexican
            Indians (Mayas and Tarahumaras). Middle American Pamphlets
            No. 2. In: Middle American Research Series Publication No.
            5, pp. 27-42. New Orleans: Tulane University of Louisiana,
            Department of Middle American Research.

Matson, G. Albin
    1970   Distribution of Blood Groups. In: T. D. Stewart, ed.,
            Physical Anthropology, pp. 105-147. Handbook of Middle
            American Indians, Vol. 9. Austin: University of Texas
            Press.

Mourant, A. E.; Ada C. Kopeć; and Kazimiera Domaniewska-Sobczak
    1958   The ABO Blood Groups. Oxford: Blackwell Scientific
            Publications.

Pennington, Campbell W.
    1963   The Tarahumar of Mexico: Their Environment and Material
            Culture. Salt Lake City: University of Utah Press.

Rodríguez, Hector; Elisa de Rodríguez; Alvar Loría; and Ruben Lisker
    1963   Studies on Several Genetic Hematological Traits of the Mexi-
            can Population: V. Distribution of Blood Group Antigens in
            Nahuas, Yaquis, Tarahumaras, Tarascos and Mixtecos. Human
            Biology 35(3):350-360.

Snyder, Richard G.; Albert A. Dahlberg; Clyde C. Snow; and Thelma
    Dahlberg
    1969   Trait Analysis of the Dentition of the Tarahumara Indians
            and Mestizos of the Sierra Madre Occidental, Mexico.
            American Journal of Physical Anthropology 31(1):65-76.

Ubelaker, Douglas H.
    1978   Human Skeletal Remains: Excavation, Analysis,
            Interpretation. Chicago: Aldine Publishing Co.

BLOOD TYPING OF TISSUE FROM FOUR MUMMIES BY THE MIXED CELL AGGLUTINATION METHOD

Donald Pate

INTRODUCTION

Blood typing of mummified tissue provides information about the genetic composition of past populations. Blood type frequencies are important in determining genetic similarities among different populations.

Blood typing of tissue is possible because ABH antigens are widely distributed throughout the human body independent of whether the person is a secretor or non-secretor. There are two distinct forms of antigens (Race and Sanger 1975): 1) a water soluble form not present in the red cells or serum but present in the body fluids and organs of a secretor, the secretion of these antigens being controlled by a pair of alleles (Se, se) which are inherited independently of the ABO genes; and 2) an alcohol soluble form present in all tissues (except the brain) and on the red cells but not present in the secretions. This form is not influenced by the secretor gene.

The purpose of this paper is to report the results of blood tests performed on tissue from four mummies from the Greater Southwest of North America--an Anasazi (Basketmaker II) infant, a Fremont adult, and an adolescent and a child from southwestern Chihuahua, Mexico. The two mummies from Chihuahua are of undetermined cultural affiliation but are from an area now occupied by the Tarahumara.

MATERIALS

The mummified tissue was supplied by the San Diego Museum of Man. The mummies had been naturally desiccated and had been found in caves.

The Anasazi infant was from southern Utah and the Fremont adult was found near Hanksville in southeastern Utah. The Chihuahuan mummies were found in the Sierra Madre Occidental of Mexico near the 28th parallel at an elevation of 2,000 meters. This area is the western boundary of the present-day Tarahumara. The Chihuahuan adolescent was radiocarbon dated at 860 ± 40 years B.P., calibrated to A.D. 1040-1260, using 15 grams of fiber from the associated string skirt (Tyson, this volume). The child (not dated) was found in the same cave but was not directly associated with the adolescent.

METHODS

The mummified epidermis was typed using the mixed cell agglutination method (Coombs et al. 1956; Lippold 1971).

Anti-A and anti-B sera were added to two test tubes containing the unknown epidermal cells from the mummified tissue, and the free cells were washed with sterile buffered saline (0.85%) until the supernatant showed no agglutination with detector erythrocytes. This ensured that any remaining antibodies were bound specifically to the antigens on the cell membranes. The free ends of the bound antibodies could now act as receptors with affinity for their specific antigens.

The test tubes were divided into two lots, and trypsinized group A and B erthrocytes were added to a tube from each lot. Each tube was labeled with a number so that the tests would be blind. The antigens on the membranes of these known erythrocytes would bind specifically with the free ends of the antibodies producing an antigen-antibody-antigen cross linkage. This agglutination reaction is possible because the mummified epidermal cells and the erythrocytes possess a common antigen. The agglutination with the known erythrocytes identifies the blood type of the mummy. There should be only one agglutination reaction in each group of tubes except when the blood is type AB, and two tubes showed positive results. The positive agglutination reaction is identified by observing one drop of the mixed cell solution under a light microscope at 250X.

Controls were set up using autopsy tissue and buccal epithelium of known ABO types to provide standard agglutination reactions.

RESULTS

The mummified epidermis showed no agglutination with anti-A and anti-B sera; therefore, the mummies were type O. The controls were all identified correctly (Tables 1 and 2).

Table 1

Results of Blind Blood Tests on Mummified Tissue

Antibody Added	Erythrocyte Added	01	02	03	04	05	06	07	08	09	10	11
anti-A	A	+	-	-	-	-	-	-	-	-	+	-
anti-A	B	-	-	-	-	-	-	-	-	-	-	-
anti-B	A	-	-	-	-	-	-	-	-	-	-	-
anti-B	B	-	-	-	-	-	-	-	-	-	-	-
Blood Type		A	O	O	O	O	O	O	O	O	A	O

Tube Number	Specimen
01	Type A Control (Autopsy Tissue)
02, 06	Chihuahuan Child
03, 07	Fremont Adult
04, 08	Anasazi Infant
05, 09	Chihuahuan Adolescent
10	Type A Control (Buccal)
11	Type O Control (Autopsy Tissue)

Table 2

ABO Determinations on Mummified Tissue

Specimen Origin	Cultural Affiliation	Sex, Age	Blood Group	
			Test 1	Test 2
S.E. Utah	Fremont* A.D. 900-1300	M, Adult	O	O
S. Utah	Anasazi** (Basketmaker II) A.D. 1-500	Infant	O	O
S.W. Chihuahua	Unknown A.D. 1040-1260 years	F, Adolescent	O	O
S.W. Chihuahua	Unknown	F, Child	O	O

*On loan to San Diego Museum of Man from Fowler-Mills Gallery, Santa
 Monica, California.
**San Diego Museum of Man catalogue number 10849.

DISCUSSION

The presence of 100% type O blood in the tissue of four mummies
from the Greater Southwest supports the known distribution of blood
types in this area. The frequency of the O gene is over 95% in South
American and Mexican populations. The small percentage of A and B genes
present were probably not introduced until the arrival of the Europeans.
Most Native Americans north of the Mexican border have primarily A and O
genes, and the low incidence of the B gene is again accounted for by
European and also African admixture. The A gene is present with frequencies above 10% in Canadian and United States native populations and
generally decreases southward. The highest A gene frequencies are in
Canadian populations--the Blackfoot and Blood Indians have A frequencies
of over 50% (Mourant, Kopeć, and Domaniewska-Sobczak 1976). Blood tests
on 55 Southwestern United States mummies resulted in 89% type O and 11%
type A (Boyd and Boyd 1937).

Experimental conditions were not optimal due to limited supplies and
tissue. Two false erythrocyte-erythrocyte agglutinations (A cells) also
occurred in the tubes of the Chihuahuan child because of the presence of
free antibodies due to insufficient washing. This type of reaction is
easily distinguished from a positive A reaction by the absence of
erythrocyte-epidermal cell agglutination.

Further problems that could be encountered in mixed cell agglutination blood typing involve the leaching and decomposition of antigens and
the presence of foreign molecules that react like antigens. Water soluble antigens can be lost by leaching while the tissue is buried in the
soil (Smith 1960). This would result in a weak, possibly nondetectable
reaction or no agglutination at all. Antigens can also be decomposed by
bacterial and protozoan enzymes. The reaction of the enzymes results in
the loss of A and B specificity and the development of H specificity
(Watkins 1956). *Clostridium tertium* produces an A-decomposing enzyme,

and *C. maebashi* produces a B-decomposing enzyme. Tissue contaminated by these organisms would be incorrectly typed as O. The presence of an H-decomposing enzyme has also been reported in *Bacillus fulminans* and *B. cereus* (Iseki 1962). Bacteria, viruses, and parasites possess molecules on their cellular surfaces that are very similar to the A and B antigens (sugar molecules) and therefore react with anti-A and anti-B antibodies. These foreign molecules would also interfere with blood typing (Weiss and Mann 1981).

Mummified tissue can be cultured and plated to check for any bacterial enzymatic decomposition and/or antigen-like surface molecules, but this was not done due to time limitations. The tissue was exposed to a 37 degree centigrade water bath for 45 minutes after trypsinization to reduce any enzymatic activity.

Further spatial and temporal studies of gene frequencies of Native Americans by the blood typing of mummified tissue could lead to a better understanding of the migration patterns of past populations, but more data are needed.

ACKNOWLEDGMENTS

I would like to thank Dr. Robert W. Astarita of the Veterans Administration Medical Center, San Diego, for the autopsy control tissue. My thanks also to Dr. Roger Sabbadini of San Diego State University for the use of his homogenizer, and especially to Dr. Lois K. Lippold of San Diego State University for her advice and assistance throughout the project.

REFERENCES CITED

Boyd, William C., and Lyle G. Boyd
   1937   Blood Grouping Tests on 300 Mummies. Journal of Immunology 32:(4)307-319.

Coombs, R. R. A.; Donald Bedford; and L. M. Rouillard
   1956   A and B Blood-Group Antigens on Human Epidermal Cells Demonstrated by Mixed Agglutination. Lancet 270:461-463.

Iseki, S.
   1962   Blood Group Specific Decomposing Enzymes from Bacteria. Bibliotheca Haematologica 13:215-218.

Lippold, Lois K.
   1971   The Mixed Cell Agglutination Method for Typing Mummified Human Tissue. American Journal of Physical Anthropology 34:377-384.

Mourant, A. E.; Ada C. Kopeć; and Kazimiera Domaniewska-Sobczak
   1976   The Distribution of the Human Blood Groups and Other Polymorphisms. London: Oxford University Press.

Pennington, Campbell W.
    1963   The Tarahumar of Mexico: Their Environment and Material
            Culture. Salt Lake City: University of Utah Press.

Race, R. R., and Ruth Sanger
    1975   Blood Groups in Man. Oxford: Blackwell Scientific
            Publications.

Smith, Madeleine
    1960   Blood Groups of the Ancient Dead. Science 131:699-702.

Watkins, Winifred M.
    1956   The Appearance of H Specificity Following the Enzymic
            Inactivation of Blood Group B Substance. Biochemical
            Journal 64:21P-22P.

Weiss, Mark L., and Alan E. Mann
    1981   Human Biology and Behavior: An Anthropological Perspective.
            Boston: Little, Brown and Co.

USE OF COMPUTER ASSISTED TOMOGRAPHY
IN THE STUDY OF A FEMALE MUMMY
FROM CHIHUAHUA, MEXICO

Anne Marie Luibel-Hulen

INTRODUCTION

Initially, paleopathological studies of mummies involved microscopic analysis obtained through tissue sampling or perhaps a complete autopsy. Autopsies employ intensive anatomical dissection and microsurgery (Cockburn et al. 1975) and, unfortunately, are destructive to the very object under investigation. The conventional radiological examination gives a relatively crude soft tissue density and spatial orientation of the object viewed. The application of a conventional radiological technique combined with an innovation in radiographic study, Computer Assisted Tomography (CAT) scan, gives a more detailed reconstruction of the anatomical and macroscopic structure of the subject.

Through the use of a mobile X-ray source, a detector system, and a computer to analyze the absorption of the X-rays, an image of both soft tissue and bone is produced (Carter et al. 1977; Gambarelli et al. 1977). The disadvantage of this approach is that it lacks microscopic detail; however, if a multidisciplinary method is used, small tissue samples can be used for histological investigation in conjunction with the application of the CAT scan. Such an approach was employed by the team of researchers examining the female mummy under study. The advantage of using a CAT scan is acquisition of knowledge without destruction of the specimen.

Two scanning sessions, using stationary units, were performed on a female mummy from Chihuahua, Mexico: the first, on January 9, 1981, at Coast Radiology, San Diego, California, using a Searle-PhoTrax 4000; the second, on November 26, 1981, at Sharp Cabrillo Hospital, San Diego, using an EMI 5005. Similar studies have been performed on Egyptian mummies (Harwood-Nash 1979) and on a series of 6 mummies from southeastern Utah (Wong 1981).

METHOD

The mummy was presented feet first to the gantry of the CAT scan aperture. The scans were taken perpendicularly to the horizontal plane of the mummy's body, which was examined in its entirety from the feet to the head and shoulders in the axial transverse plane (Figure 1). Great care in alignment to the gantry was necessary to obtain a complete transverse view of each section. The images required careful interpretation due to the flexed position of the lower limbs. Particular scans of the head were taken in the sagittal plane.

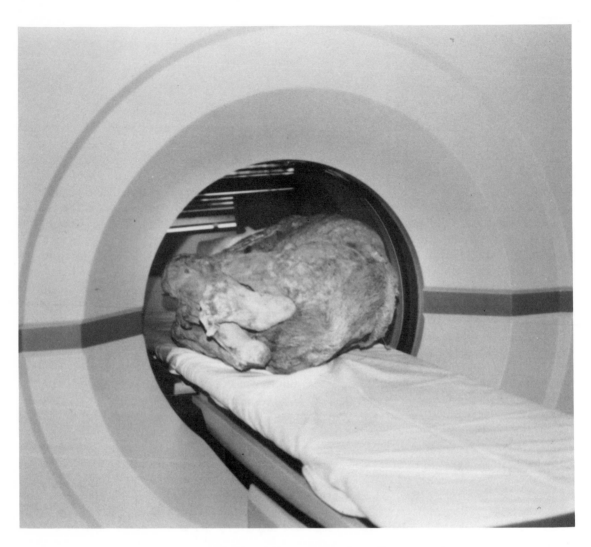

Figure 1. Female mummy emerging from gantry
(first scanning session).

The scanning diameter was 45 cm; thus, the initial scan, beginning at the feet, viewed a transverse section 1 cm thick encompassing the entire diameter of the mummy. Each succeeding scan was of the same thickness, with an interval of 1 cm between scans. In all, 22 scans were taken in the axial transverse plane (Figure 2) and 10 in the sagittal plane of the head region. The images were viewed on the screen of the computer terminal as they were taken and then photographed for detailed analysis. During the second scanning session, 10 months later, 6 transverse views of the pelvic region were taken.

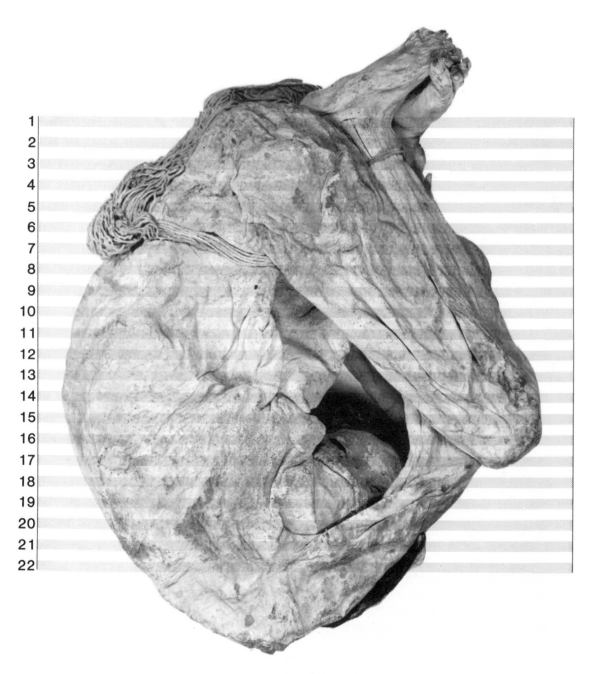

Figure 2.   Approximate sites of transverse sections
(first scanning session).

DISCUSSION

For the purpose of this paper it is unnecessary to discuss each scan; there are, however, some specific discoveries that do merit attention. In the cranial cavity, scans taken in the sagittal plane disclose a small, dense area of material which is probably desiccated brain tissue (Figure 3). In the transverse scans of the head area, the cervical vertebrae appear normal and show no signs of having undergone stress.

A sagittal section of the head region reveals that the right mandibular condyle does not articulate with the temporomandibular fossa (Figure 4). This results in the mandible protruding beyond the maxilla (see

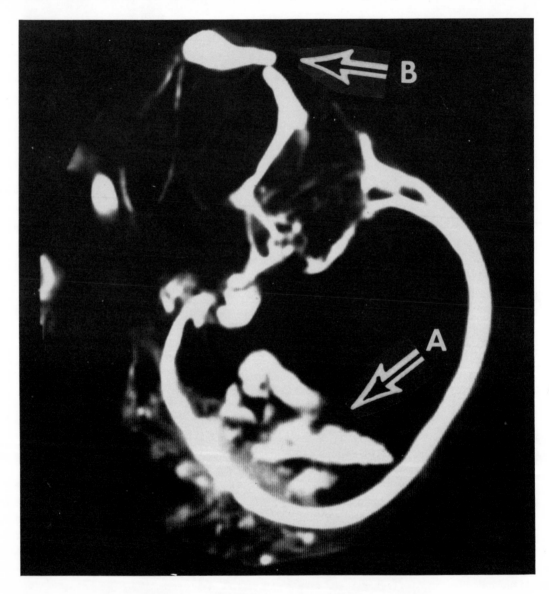

Figure 3. Sagittal scan of head area
showing desiccated brain tissue (arrow A)
and malocclusion of mandible (arrow B).

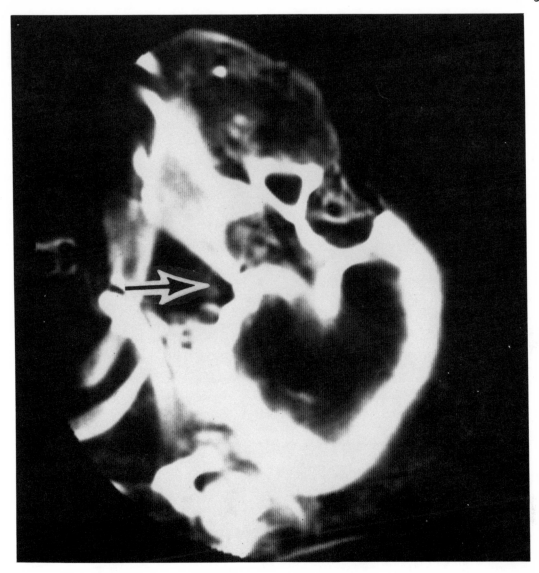

Figure 4. Scan of temporomandibular region
showing anterior dislocation of mandible (arrow).

also Figure 3). This may have been a post-mortem occurrence resulting
from positioning during burial or loosening of the connective tissue
with the mandible falling forward.

All the vertebrae (cervical, thoracic, and lumbar) appear normal.
The ribs are intact and undamaged. The scans show remnants of thoracic
organs (heart and lungs), but these are indistinct and appear as thin,
shadowy areas (Figure 5). There is also an indication of abdominal organs. These appear denser than those in the thorax; however, they too
are individually undefinable (Figure 6). Some scans show what may be
remains of the spinal cord in the vertebral foramen (Figure 7).

The scans show no fractures of the long bones, and the medullary
cavities of the femora and tibiae are quite distinct (Figures 5-7). The
ulnae and radii appear normal, as do the bones of the hands and feet.

40

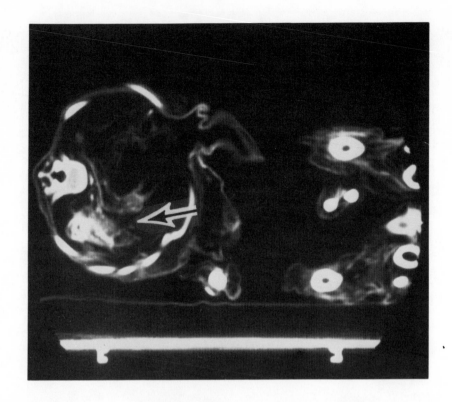

Figure 5. Scan 12 showing thoracic organs.

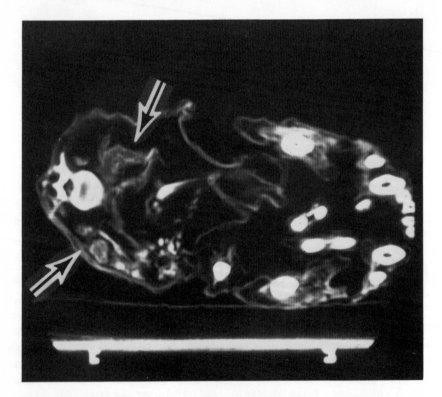

Figure 6. Scan 9 showing abdominal organs.

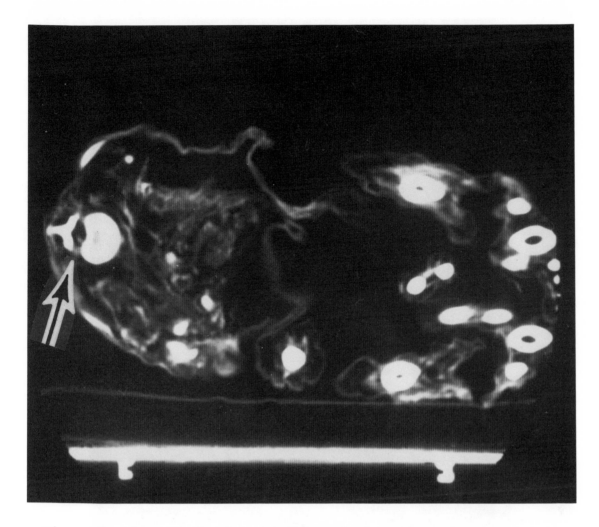

Figure 7. Scan 10 showing possible spinal cord remains (arrow).

Transverse scans of the pelvis show fetal remains (Figures 8-10) with skull bones and ribs distinguishable. The mummy's pubic symphysis and right hip are dislocated (Figures 9 and 10); this could be either an ante- or a post-mortem occurrence. If this individual had entered the process of childbirth, hormones would have relaxed the cartilage of the pubic symphysis, and this might account for its dislocation. Or, the joining cartilages of the pelvic girdle, through time, might have lost their connective properties, resulting in post-mortem dislocations.

This discovery necessitated further investigation, and the second scanning of the pelvic region was undertaken in order to show all the bones of the pelvic girdle in one scan. In this session, 6 transverse, 1 cm scans were taken beginning at the iliac crest and progressing downwards. Examination of the scans revealed the following deformity: a forward shift of the right innominate with concomitant dislocations of the pubic symphysis, right hip (Figure 11), and right sacroiliac joint (Figure 12). Whether this trauma was induced before or after death is not known.

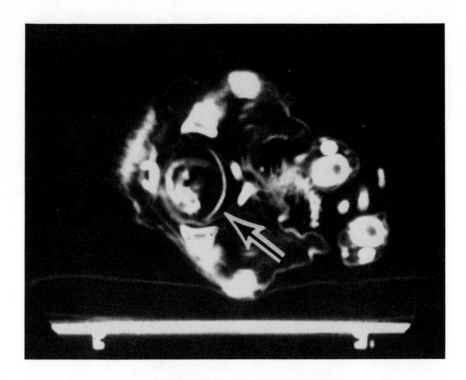

Figure 8. Scan 2 showing fetal skull bones
low in pelvic area (arrow).

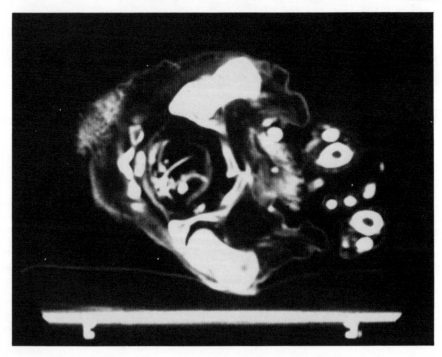

Figure 9. Scan 3 showing dislocations
of pubic symphysis and right hip
(see also Figure 10).

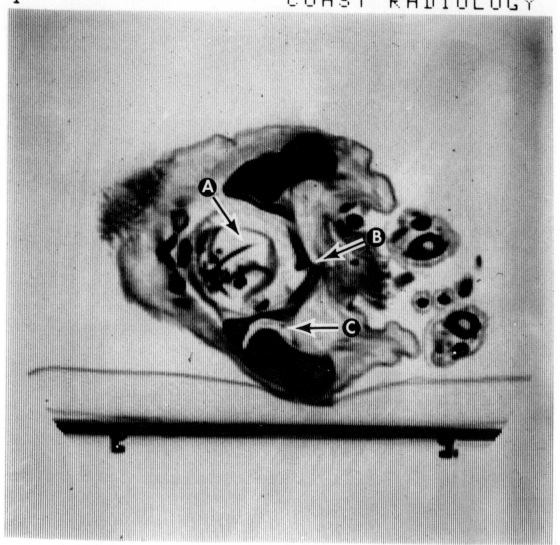

Figure 10. Enlargement of scan 3 showing fetal bones
in pelvic area (arrow A), dislocation of pubic symphysis (arrow B),
and dislocation of right femoral head from the acetabulum (arrow C).

44

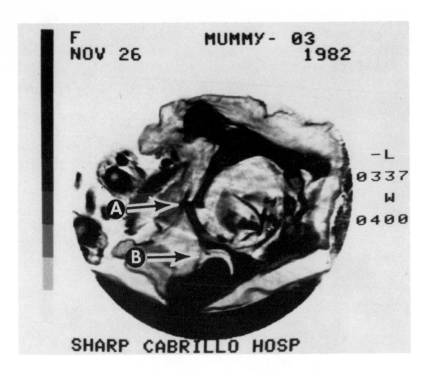

Figure 11. Scan showing dislocations of pubic
symphysis (arrow A) and right hip (arrow B).

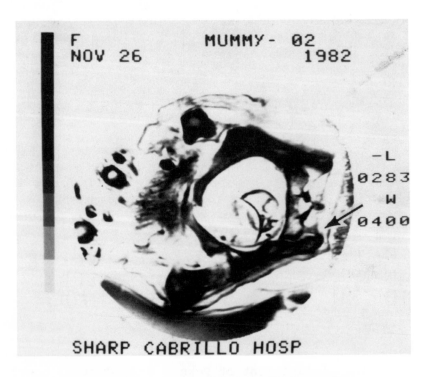

Figure 12. Scan showing dislocation
of right sacroiliac joint (arrow).

APPLICATION

The computer of the CAT scan apparatus has other capabilities in addition to those of section image reconstruction. By using certain programs, the computer can calculate the density of any area in the scan. Density readings were taken at specific points on the mummy: skull, brain material, rib, vertebrae, thoracic area, breast region, femoral head, and leg muscle. All were recorded, but lacking comparative data, no interpretations have been proposed. Attempts have been made to establish standard density values for normal and pathological mummified tissues (Pahl 1980; Wong 1981). The computer can also measure objects (such as thoracic width) in the scan and give specific physical measurements. The biparietal diameter of the fetal skull was measured at approximately 4.5 cm; according to data from Kurtz (1980), this indicates an estimated gestation age of 28-32 weeks. Another valuable aspect of the CAT scan computer is its ability to store information. All scans taken of the mummy are stored on computer discs and can be recalled at any time. It is not necessary to repeat the procedure because investigations can be made using the stored data. This is important as the specimen might not always be available for research.

CONCLUSION

The CAT scan images give a detailed, internal picture of the anatomy and macroscopic structure of the mummy. As the reservoir of comparative data grows, there will be a greater opportunity to explore the potential of Computer Assisted Tomography. Use of this technique creates a complement between the old and the new by allowing fresh knowledge to be gained without destroying the source.

ACKNOWLEDGMENTS

I sincerely thank Dr. Norman Silverman and Dr. Larry Goldberger for the generous use of the CAT scan machines and their assistance throughout the project. I extend gratitude to Laurie Rush, Lonnie Gureczy, and Mary Olson for their technical expertise in the operation of the equipment. My warmest appreciation goes to my father, Dr. F. Joseph Luibel, for his considerable aid in this analysis.

REFERENCES CITED

Carter, Barbara; James Morehead; Samuel Wolpert; Steven Hammerschlag;
    Harry Griffiths; and Paul Kahn
    1977   Crossectional Anatomy: Computed Tomography and Ultrasound
            Correlation. New York: Appleton-Century-Crofts.

Cockburn, Aidan; Robin Barraco; Theodore Reyman; and William Peck
    1975   Autopsy of an Egyptian Mummy. Science 187(4182):1155-1160.

Gambarelli, J.; G. Guerinel; L. Chevrot; and M. Mattei
    1977   Computerized Axial Tomography, an Atlas of Serial Sections of
            the Human Body, Anatomy-Radiology-Scanner. Berlin,
            Heidelberg, and New York: Springer-Verlag.

Harwood-Nash, Derek C. F.
    1979   Computed Tomography of Ancient Egyptian Mummies. Journal of
            Computer Assisted Tomography 3(6):768-773.

Kurtz, Alfred B.
    1980   Analysis of Biparietal Diameter as an Accurate Indication of
            Gestation Age. Journal of Clinical Ultrasound 8:319-326.

Pahl, Wolfgang Michael
    1980   Computed Tomography--A New Radiodiagnostical Technique
            Applied to Medico-Archaelogical Investigation of Egyptian
            Mummies. OSSA (International Journal of Skeletal Research)
            7:189-198. Stockholm: University of Stockholm.

Wong, Patricia A.
    1981   Computed Tomography in Paleopathology: Technique and Case
            Study. American Journal of Physical Anthropology 55(1):
            101-110.

HISTOLOGICAL ESTIMATION OF AGE AT DEATH
OF A FEMALE MUMMY
FROM CHIHUAHUA, MEXICO

D. D. Thompson and S. B. Laughlin

INTRODUCTION

The use of histological methods in estimating age at death has been shown to be accurate when applied to mummies (Thompson and Cowen 1983; Thompson, Cowen, and Laughlin 1985; Zimmerman et al. 1981). Single mummies (Zimmerman et al. 1981), family units of mummies (Thompson and Cowen 1983; Thompson, Cowen, and Laughlin 1985), and entire communities of intentionally mummified remains (Beman n.d.; Thompson, Beman, and Laughlin n.d.) have been analyzed by the histological methods of Thompson (1979).

In addition to the estimation of age at death, a number of other variables derived from the histological analysis of the bone yield valuable insight into the bone metabolism of the individual prior to death. These include the amount of bone mass, the quality of bone, and generalized metabolic pathologies that may have affected a person prior to death. Bone disorders such as primary or secondary hyperparathyroidism, osteomalacia, and osteoporosis would be apparent from this analysis.

The method of sampling mummified bone tissue is an important consideration. Well preserved mummies are rare, and the opportunity to obtain post-mortem biopsies from mummies is even more rare. The invasive techniques employed in obtaining biopsies must minimize the tissue destruction while maximizing the information derived. The bone core technique (Thompson 1979) has been found to satisfy a number of requisite conditions in the analysis of mummies. The sample required for analysis is small--a single bone core measuring about 0.5 cm in diameter. The variables derived from the bone core analysis are summarized below. The small amount of tissue needed and the information that is derived from the analysis of the bone core have made this method of sampling well received by museum curators, physical anthropologists, law enforcement officers, coroners, and medical examiners.

Another important consideration in the analysis of mummified remains and the interpretation of findings is a comparative data base in which to compare and place into context the findings from the analysis of a single mummy or skeleton. A single data point from a single skeleton is of little use if not placed into context with a larger population analyzed in the identical manner, optimally from either a genetically-related or geographically contiguous population in which the age at death, sex, morbidity, and cause of death are known. In this way, any substantial deviation encountered in the analysis of a single specimen can be better interpreted. The bone core technique has been applied to 3,000+ individual skeletons and on multiple bones from most skeletons. Approximately 1,500 of these skeletons were of known age, sex, race, morbidity, and cause and time of death. The remaining skeletons had

48

age, sex, and race assigned by traditional, morphological techniques. Of the 1,500 individuals without known age, sex, and race, about 260 individuals were mummies from Alaska, Greenland, and Peru.

The purpose of this study is to perform, by histological methods, an estimation of age at death of a female mummy from Chihuahua, Mexico, and to assess the bone cores for bone mass and other histological variables that will aid in interpreting this individual's bone metabolism prior to and leading up to her death.

MATERIALS AND METHODS

Three bone cores, each measuring 3.60 mm in diameter, were removed from the anterior femoral midshaft of the female Chihuahuan mummy. The bone cores were removed with the aid of a high speed, hand held drill and a specially designed bone corer.

The cortical thickness of the femur was measured from the intact cores to the nearest 0.05 mm with dental calipers. Next, the endosteal (inner) surface of the cores was ground down to a flat surface, resulting in nearly perfect, cylindrically shaped cores of bone. Core volumes could then be determined by the formula $\pi r^2 h$. The weights of the cores were recorded to the nearest 0.0001 gm, and the cortical bone density (gm/cm^3) was then calculated as the weight of the core divided by the volume. Each core was then sectioned in a plane transverse to the longitudinal axis of the femur, and two 100-micron sections were cut from each core and mounted on microscope slides. Five histological features, apparent in microscopic viewing of the thin sections, were measured in each thin section (Figure 1). The five features were: secondary osteon

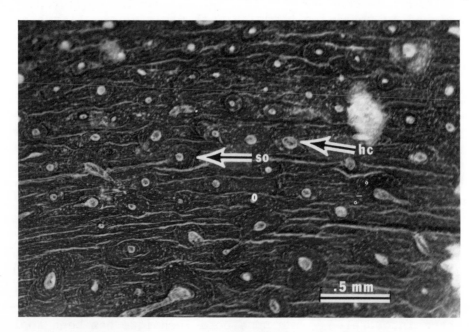

Figure 1. Thin section, anterior midshaft of the femur, showing secondary osteons (so) and Haversian canals (hc).

area, secondary osteon perimeter, Haversian canal area, Haversian canal perimeter, and secondary osteon number. The method used in quantifying each of the histological features is presented in Thompson and Galvin (1983). Age at death estimates were determined by use of the following regression equation (Thompson 1979:907, Table 3): age (in years) = 101.9(x) + 6.68 years, where x is equal to secondary osteon number times secondary osteon area.

RESULTS

The data derived from the intact bone cores from the Chihuahuan mummy are presented in Table 1.

Table 1

Intact Core Variables

	Cortical Thickness (mm)	Core Weight (gm)	Core Density (gm/cm^3)
Core 1	4.20	0.0743	1.872
Core 2	4.20	0.0743	1.872
Core 3*	4.35	0.0732	1.921

*site is 2.5 cm distal from midshaft

The data derived from the quantification of the histological structures in one thin section from each bone core are presented in Table 2.

Table 2

Histological Variables

	Secondary Osteon Area (mm^2)	Secondary Osteon Perimeter (mm)	Haversian Canal Area (mm^2)	Haversian Canal Perimeter (mm)	Secondary Osteon Number (per mm^2)
Core 1	0.0183	0.4807	0.0012	0.1328	3.67
Core 2	0.0209	0.5184	0.0023	0.1872	4.00
Core 3*	0.0148	0.4263	0.0014	0.1298	10.67

*site is 2.5 cm distal from midshaft

The estimated ages at death obtained from the analysis of the three sections are contained in Table 3.

Table 3

Estimated Ages at Death
for the Chihuahuan Female Mummy

	Estimated Ages at Death (yrs)
Core 1	13.5
Core 2	15.2
Core 3*	22.8

*site is 2.5 cm distal from midshaft

DISCUSSION

The cortical thickness values obtained from the Chihuahuan mummy were less than cortical thickness values obtained for similarly aged Caucasian and Black females (Thompson et al. 1982) but were comparable to cortical thickness values obtained for similarly aged females from the Pecos Pueblo skeletal series (a group of skeletons from the same geographical region but predating this mummy) (Thompson, unpublished data). Although the cortical thickness values are less than other populations, they are fully compatible with the Pecos Pueblo and do not reflect any systemic bone loss pathologies. This conclusion also finds support in the density values, where they are well within the normal range of 1.60 - 2.10 gm/cm^3 derived from analyses of different populations of known age, sex, and cause of death (Thompson, Salter, and Laughlin 1981:92).

Histological analysis and the age estimation indicated the skeleton to be young, i.e., less than 20 years of age. The secondary osteon area and perimeter were also well within normal limits. The Haversian canal area and perimeter were unremarkable and showed no bone remodeling pathologies or deficiencies, and thus no pronounced systemic defects in bone metabolism.

The age estimates derived from the analysis of bone cores 1 and 2 were very similar while the estimate from bone core 3 was older. A partial explanation for the discrepancies in the three estimates performed on cores from the same general location may be that bone core 3 was taken distal to the midshaft. The standards of age estimation by histological methods have been established precisely at the midshaft of the femur.

CONCLUSIONS

The bone core technique was used in the analysis of bone samples from a mummy from Chihuahua, Mexico. The results of this study indicated that the female was approximately 15 years of age and had no apparent metabolic bone disease. Each variable examined showed the bone to be normal when compared with similarly aged females from nearby skeletal populations and with similarly aged females from other populations.

REFERENCES CITED

Beman, S. B.
  n.d.   Skeletal Biology of the Kagamil Aleut Mummies. Ph.D.
         Dissertation in preparation, University of Connecticut,
         Storrs.

Thompson, D. D.
  1979   The Core Technique in the Determination of Age at Death in
         Skeletons. Journal of Forensic Sciences 26:902-915.

Thompson, D. D.; S. B. Beman; and W. S. Laughlin
  n.d.   Histomorphometric Analysis of Cortical Bone from the Kagamil
         Aleut Mummies. In preparation.

Thompson, D. D., and K. S. Cowen
  1983   Age at Death and Bone Biology of the Barrow Mummies. Paper
         presented at the Symposium on the Frozen Family of Barrow.
         Alaska Anthropological Annual Meeting, March 11, 1983,
         Anchorage, Alaska.

Thompson, D. D.; K. S. Cowen; and S. B. Laughlin
  1985   Estimation of Age at Death and Histomorphometric Analysis of
         Cortical and Trabecular Bone Samples of Greenland Mummies.
         Meddelelser om Grønland. Copenhagen. In press.

Thompson, D. D., and C. A. Galvin
  1983   Estimation of Age at Death by Tibial Osteon Remodeling in an
         Autopsy Series. International Journal of Forensic Sciences
         22:203-211.

Thompson, D. D.; A. B. Harper; W. S. Laughlin; and J. B. Jorgensen
  1982   Bone Loss in Eskimos. In: B. Harvald and J. P. Hart, eds.,
         Circumpolar Health 81, Proceedings of the 5th International
         Symposium on Circumpolar Health. Nordic Council for Arctic
         Medical Research Report Series No. 33. Copenhagen.

Thompson, D. D,; E. M. Salter; and W. S. Laughlin
    1981   Bone Core Analysis of Baffin Island Skeletons. Arctic
            Anthropology 18(1):87-96.

Zimmerman, M. R.; E. R. Trinkaus; M. LeMay; A. C. Aufderheide; T. A.
    Reyman; G. R. Marrocco; R. W. Ortel; J. T. Benitez; W. S. Laughlin;
    P. D. Horne; R. E. Schultes; and E. A. Coughlin
    1981   The Paleopathology of an Aleutian Mummy. Archives of
            Pathology and Laboratory Medicine 105:638-641. Chicago.

PRELIMINARY ASSESSMENT
OF PROTEIN-CALORIE DEFICIENCY
IN MUMMIFIED SCALP TISSUE
FROM CHIHUAHUA, MEXICO

Nelly Canedo

INTRODUCTION

Malnutrition is the most pressing health problem confronting populations undergoing cultural transition and/or urbanization (Frisancho 1979); it may also have played an important role in the decline of ancient populations (Steinbock 1976). Therefore, the identification of dietary protein and calorie deficiencies provides information of clinical, social, economic, political, and historical value.

Protein-calorie malnutrition (PCM) is a condition in which insufficient protein and calorie intake can result in deficits in immunity response as well as in growth and development (Jelliffe 1955, 1966; Bradfield 1972; Frisancho 1979). The form of PCM known as *kwashiorkor* is particularly marked by a severe response to acute protein deficiency; however, *marasmus*, produced by the chronic reduction of all nutrients, is a more significant health problem and has a relative importance at the population level that is probably underestimated (Jelliffe 1966; Bradfield 1972; Frisancho 1979).

For extinct populations, bones were once the only element of diagnosis of nutritional deficiencies. These deficiencies could be identified as: 1) transverse lines, also called growth arrest lines (Asada 1924; Harris 1933); and 2) sieve-like porosities known as spongy hyperostosis (Hamperl and Weiss 1955) or porotic hyperostosis (Angel 1966, 1967). Deprivation of protein and calories, however, produces morphological and physiological changes first in protein-rich tissues rather than in bone. Hair is a protein-rich tissue with enormous daily metabolic requirements; hence, it is the first tissue affected by dietary deficiencies (Bradfield 1972). The rate of proliferation of hair root cells is one of the most rapid in the body--a complete cycle of reduplication occurs every 12 to 24 hours (Van Scott, Ekel, and Auerbach 1963; Ackerman 1978). Each hair follicle produces approximately 0.35 mm of hair per day (Montagna and Parakkal 1974), enabling analysis of hair to be used not only for the early diagnosis of PCM, but also for discrimination between its two forms: acute and chronic.

For living populations, the World Health Organization has selected eleven diagnostic characteristics of PCM (Jelliffe 1966:16, 43-48). Four of these characteristics are based on measurement of hair, which is the first tissue to be influenced by dietary variations (Montagna 1956; Bradfield, Bailey, and Margen 1967; Bradfield 1968, 1971). The technique developed by Bradfield (1968) consists of microscopic examination of hair removed from the scalp. The degree of PCM is assessed by the stage of growth of the hair and the morphological differences between those hair follicles which are in various stages of growth. In the case of mummified tissue, which is desiccated, the hair is too brittle for such individual examination; thus, a modification of Bradfield's technique was needed for use in samples of scalp extracted from mummified tissue.

METHOD

A sample, approximately 3.0 x 3.5 cm, was excised from the occipital region of the mummy's scalp. This tissue was rehydrated in a solution of formalin-alcohol-sodium carbonate (Allison and Gerszten 1977; Reyman 1978; Reyman and Dowd 1980). The rehydrated tissue was embedded in paraffin to facilitate slicing (5 micron sections). Sections, mounted on slides, were stained with trichrome (Masson's trichrome), hematoxylin (Periodic acid-Schiff, PAS) as described in Luna (1968), and eosin to improve visibility of the elements of the hair root as well as the adjacent tissue.

Three characteristics were recorded for each follicle under microscopic examination: dimension, pigmentation, and position (depth in epithelium). The last characteristic was added to those established by Bradfield (1968) to assess hair growth in sections of the scalp. Hair growth is cyclical, and the active follicles periodically undergo involutionary changes, entering a period of quiescence or rest. After variable intervals, the resting follicles burst into activity again, a new follicle forms, and the production of a new hair begins. The growing, involutionary, and resting phases are called, respectively: anagen, catagen, and telogen (Dry in Montagna 1956; Montagna and Parakkal 1974). In the present study, the anagen phase was distinguished by: 1) follicles with the largest cross section (anagens are typically twice the area of catagens or telogens); 2) strong, distinctive pigmentation; and 3) location in the dermis of the epithelium. Only follicles meeting all three of these criteria were classified as anagens (Figures 1 and 2).

DISCUSSION

Based on the analysis of 93 hair follicles in 40 slides, 18% were anagen hair roots, indicating a maximum sum of 82% for catagens and telogens. This is a low estimate for the anagen frequency because of the restricting definition of anagens (by size, pigmentation, and position) and the loss of anagens in the slicing process.

In normal nutritional states, the frequency of anagen follicles is 80-90% (Bradfield 1972; Ackerman 1978). In acute malnutrition, the color and texture of the hair change, and the percentage of anagens decreases. The most dramatic response is found in long-term deprivation, during which, as a defensive adaptation, there is a complete shift to the resting phase of hair growth in order to maintain blood nitrogen

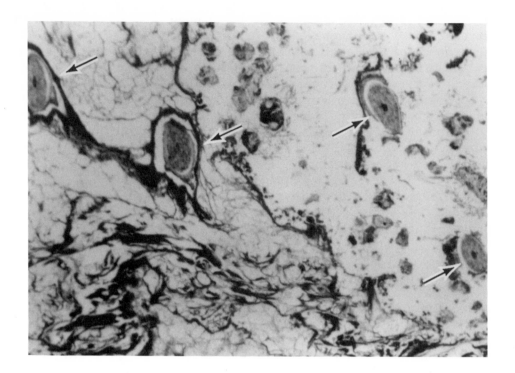

Figure 1. Cross section of anagen hair follicles from
rehydrated tissue (X60).

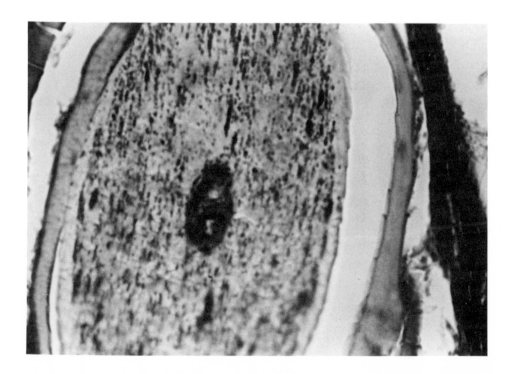

Figure 2. Cross section of anagen hair follicle (X675).

levels. In this case, the percentage of anagens drops to one and stabilizes at that level (Montagna 1956; Bradfield 1968; Ackerman 1978).

The presence of at least 18% anagens far exceeds the expected anagen count in chronic PCM but is consistent with a diagnosis of acute PCM. This mummy, however, was pregnant at the time of death (Alcauskas, this volume; Luibel-Hulen, this volume; and Pinter, this volume), and it has been observed that pregnant females have a decrease in the percentage of anagens (Montagna and Parakkal 1974). Furthermore, the bone core analysis by Thompson and Laughlin (this volume) indicates that no metabolic bone disease was present.

Protein and calorie deficiencies produce morphological and physiological changes first in protein-rich tissues such as hair. Thus, it is possible that the adult female was suffering from acute protein-calorie malnutrition--but in its initial stage.

CONCLUSION

A microscopic analysis of hair follicles removed from an adolescent female mummy from Chihuahua, Mexico, indicates that this individual may have had an acute, but recently acquired, form of protein-calorie malnutrition. Techniques used in this analysis, although relatively new, provide a valid tool in paleopathological studies. Refinement and standardization of these methods will improve and aid our understanding of nutritional and metabolic deficiences of past populations.

ACKNOWLEDGMENTS

The author wishes to thank Robin Foerster, M.D., Pathologist, Naval Hospital, San Diego, California, and F. Joseph Luibel, M.D., Pathologist, Sharp Cabrillo Hospital, San Diego, for their generous contributions of technical assistance, materials, and space for this study. Appreciation is also extended to J. Baldwin, histologic technician and B. Kersbergen, pharmacist of the Naval Hospital, San Diego, and to Robin Howard, M.D., Sharp Cabrillo Hospital, San Diego.

REFERENCES CITED

Ackerman, A. B.
    1978   Histologic Diagnosis of Inflammatory Skin Diseases: A Method
              by Pattern Analysis (especially pp. 50-63). Philadelphia:
              Lea and Febiger.

Allison, M. J., and E. Gerszten
    1977   Paleopathology in Peruvian Mummies: Application of Modern
              Techniques. Richmond, Virginia: Medical College of
              Virginia.

Angel, J. L.
    1966   Porotic Hyperostosis, Anemias, Malarias, and Marshes in the
              Prehistoric Eastern Mediterranean. Science 153:760-763.

    1967   Porotic Hyperostosis or Osteoporosis Symmetrica. In: D. R.
              Brothwell and A. T. Sandison, eds., Diseases in Antiquity,
              pp. 378-389. Springfield, Illinois: Charles C. Thomas,
              Publisher.

Asada, T.
    1924   Über die Entstehung und Pathologisch Bedeutung der im
              Röntgenbild des Rohrenknockens am Diaphysenende zum Vorschein
              Kommenden "Parallelen Querlinienbildun." Mitteilungen,
              Faculty of Medicine 9:43-95. Kyushu University, Fukuoka,
              Japan.

Bradfield, R. B.
    1968   Changes in Hair Associated with Protein-Calorie Malnutrition.
              In: R. A. McCance and E. M. Widdowson, eds., Calorie
              Deficiencies and Protein Deficiencies. Boston: Little,
              Brown and Co.

    1971   Protein Deprivation: Comparative Response of Hair Roots,
              Serum Protein, and Urinary Nitrogen. The American Journal of
              Clinical Nutrition 24:405-410.

    1972   A Rapid Tissue Technique for the Field of Assessment of
              Protein-Calorie Malnutrition. The American Journal of
              Clinical Nutrition 25:720-729.

Bradfield, R. B.; M. A. Bailey; and S. Margen
    1967   Morphological Changes in Human Scalp Hair During Deprivation
              of Protein. Science 157:438-439.

Frisancho, A. R.
    1979   Human Adaptation: A Functional Interpretation. Toronto:
              C. V. Mosby Co.

58

Hamperl, H., and P. Weiss
    1955   Über die Spongiose Hyperostose an Schädeln aus Alt-Peru.
            Archiv für Pathologische Anatomie und Physiologie und
            Klinische Medizin 327:629-642. Berlin.

Harris, H. A.
    1933   Bone Growth in Health and Disease. London: Oxford
            University Press.

Jelliffe, D. B.
    1955   Infant Nutrition in the Tropics and Subtropics. World Health
            Organization, Monograph Series No. 29.

    1966   The Assessment of the Nutritional Status of the Community.
            World Health Organization.

Luna, L. G.
    1968   Manual of Histologic Staining: Methods of the Armed Forces
            Institute of Pathology, 3rd ed. New York: McGraw Hill.

Montagna, W., ed.
    1956   The Structure and Function of Skin. New York: Academic
            Press, Inc.

Montagna, W., and P. F. Parakkal, eds.
    1974   The Structure and Function of Skin, 3rd ed. New York:
            Academic Press, Inc.

Reyman, T. A.
    1978   The Fascination of Paleopathology: Studies on Egyptian
            Mummies. Presented to the Paleopathology Club, International
            Academy of Pathology, Atlanta, Georgia, March 5, 1978.

Reyman, T. A., and A. M. Dowd
    1980   Processing of Mummified Tissue of Histological Examination.
            In: A. Cockburn and E. Cockburn, eds., Mummies, Disease, and
            Ancient Cultures, pp. 258-273. Cambridge: Cambridge
            University Press.

Steinbock, R. T.
    1976   Paleopathological Diagnosis and Interpretation. Springfield,
            Illinois: Charles C. Thomas, Publisher.

Van Scott, E. J.; T. M. Ekel; and R. Auerbach
    1963   Determinants of Rate and Kinetics of Cell Division in Scalp
            Hair. Journal of Investigative Dermatology 41:269-273.

AN INVESTIGATION INTO THE CAUSE OF DEATH
OF TWO CHIHUAHUAN MUMMIES

Elizabeth S. Dyer Alcauskas

The most commonly asked question about the Chihuahuan mummies is: How did they die? In attempting to answer this, three methods of investigation were used: direct observation, radiography, and Computer Assisted Tomography (CAT) scan. These methods were selected in an effort to determine the causes of death without damaging the specimens.

THE CHILD MUMMY

In the child mummy, there is extensive post-mortem damage--the head and the left side of the upper torso are missing (Pinter, this volume). Radiographs of the child revealed a thickening of the bone cortex of the ulna, radius, tibia, and fibula (Figure 1). In each of these bones the normal outline of the periosteum was clearly seen, as was the area of increased density formed by hyperostotic material. This particular bone lesion is termed "cloaking periostitis" and is indicative of early congenital syphilis but, by itself, is not diagnostic of that disease (Kennedy: personal communication, 1981).

Congenital syphilis is transmitted to the fetus through the mother's placenta. The first stage, early congenital syphilis, is a severe disease resulting in death 50% of the time. During this first stage, bone lesions appear anytime from birth to the age of 3 or 4 years (Steinbock 1976:98).

Two types of bone lesions occur in early congenital syphilis: periostitis and diaphyseal osteomyelitis. Periostitis is a reaction of the periosteum (the membrane surrounding the bone) to the treponemal infection of syphilis, resulting in new bone being laid down over the affected area, thus thickening the cortex in the characteristic manner of cloaking periostitis. Cloaking periostitis is sometimes associated with diaphyseal osteomyelitis, a condition whereby the thickened cortex becomes focally destroyed. When these foci of osteomyelitis are present at the proximal ends of both tibiae on their medial aspects, they are called Wimberger's sign (Steinbock 1976:99). The radiographs of the Chihuahuan child mummy show no such deterioration (Figures 2 and 3).

Of 100 children who contract congenital syphilis, only 23 to 25 will show cloaking periostitis, which definitely appears on this child, while only 1 to 3 will show both cloaking periostitis and Wimberger's sign (Steinbock 1976:99). Although a diagnosis of early congenital syphilis

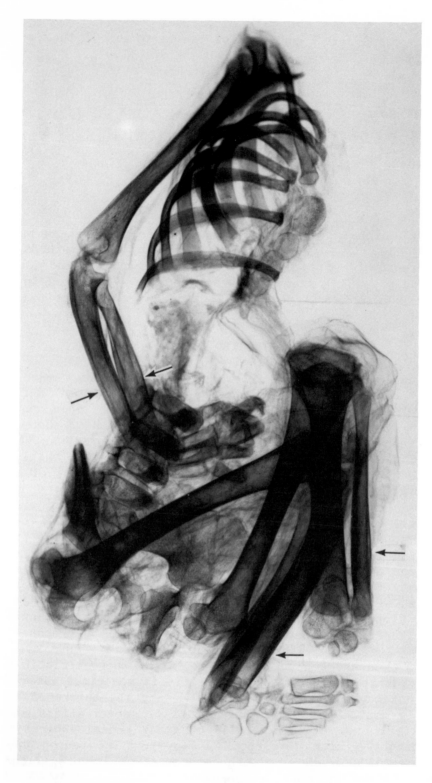

Figure 1. Radiograph of child
(arrows indicate thickening of long bones).

cannot be made, neither can it be discarded. There is currently no procedure which could detect antigens of the treponema if they were in fact
present (James Miller: personal communication, 1981).

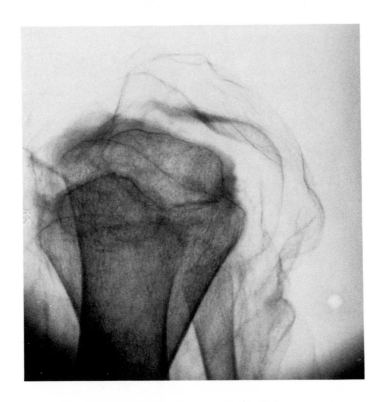

Figure 2. Left knee of child mummy.

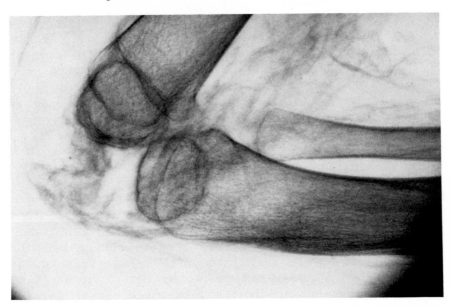

Figure 3. Right knee of child mummy.

THE ADOLESCENT FEMALE MUMMY

In the adolescent female mummy, no apparent abnormalities were noticed by direct observation. It did appear that she might have been pregnant, or might recently have given birth, because her breasts and abdomen were noticeably enlarged.

Radiographs confirm she was pregnant. The position of the fetal head--low in the pelvis--suggests she was in labor (Figure 4). The shape of the fetal head--the bones in an overriding position--also suggests she was in labor. The premature nature of the labor is indicated by the gestation age of the fetus, 28 to 32 weeks (Carson: personal communication, 1981). The estimated fetal age was determined from the biparietal measurement correlated with modern growth tables. Radiographs show that the size of the fetal head in relation to the size of the adolescent's pelvic inlet is compatible, ruling out dystocia (difficult childbirth) from cephalopelvic disproportion (Carson: personal communication, 1981).

The CAT scan also confirms the pregnancy of the mummy, as well as the age of the fetus. Furthermore, the scan shows that the sacroiliac joint of the mummy is disarticulated, a condition which had not been realized from the radiographs. As stated by Luibel-Hulen (this volume), the timing (ante-mortem or post-mortem) of this traumatic deformity of the pelvis cannot be determined. No fractures of the long bones can be seen.

The adolescent does not appear to have died as a direct result of the process of childbirth. Katherine Carson, M.D., Obstetrician/Gynecologist, suggested several medical conditions which would both induce premature labor and cause the death of the mother. Two of her suggestions seem especially applicable: a ruptured placenta and eclampsia.

A ruptured placenta would cause premature labor and the death of the mother due to loss of blood through internal hemorrhaging. A blow to the pelvic region, one strong enough to disarticulate the sacroiliac joint, would undoubtedly be strong enough to rupture the placenta.

Eclampsia, or metabolic toxemia of late pregnancy, is not uncommon today and induces premature labor and death. Eclampsia is medically defined as convulsions and coma occurring in a pregnant female and is associated with hypertension, edema, and/or proteinuria (presence of an excess of serum proteins in the urine) (Dorland 1974:491). Eclampsia occurs in the last half of pregnancy, usually in the seventh to ninth month. It is often seen today among young women, especially those in non-western cultures (Carson: personal communication, 1981). If toxins in the kidney could be found through a biopsy, it would indicate that eclampsia was a possibility. It is not known, however, if these toxins survive through time (Boylen: personal communication, 1981).

Although the cause of eclampsia is unknown, there are indications that in some cases it may be associated with malnutrition or inadequate salt intake or both. There is evidence that both malnutrition *and* inadaquate salt intake occur today in the Tarahumara region (Arrieta: personal communication, 1981). Could this have been true eight centuries ago? Canedo's analysis of hair follicles indicates the possibility of acute protein-calorie malnutrition (Canedo, this volume).

Using nondestructive techniques, only tentative conclusions can be made regarding cause of death. In the future, analyses by a team of paleopathologists may reveal the exact or contributing causes of the deaths of these individuals.

Figure 4. Female mummy showing position of fetal head.

ACKNOWLEDGMENTS

The author wishes to thank the following for their assistance: Ms. Olivia Arrieta, Department of Anthropology, University of Arizona; Dr. Lois Boylen, Department of Hematology, Orthopedic Hospital, Los Angeles; the late Dr. Katherine Carson, Ob/Gyn, Sharp Memorial Hospital, San Diego; Dr. Gail Kennedy, Department of Anthropology, University of California, Los Angeles; Dr. James Miller, School of Medicine, University of California, Los Angeles; Dr. Donald Resnick, Department of Radiology, Veterans Administration Medical Center, San Diego; and Ms. Terry Willingham, San Diego Zoo Hospital.

REFERENCES CITED

Dorland, William Alexander Newman
    1974   Dorland's Illustrated Medical Dictionary, 25th edition.
            Philadelphia: W. B. Saunders.

Steinbock, R. Ted
    1976   Paleopathological Diagnosis and Interpretation.
            Springfield, Illinois: Charles C. Thomas.

SCANNING ELECTRON MICROSCOPE STUDIES OF BOTANICAL SPECIMENS FROM A FEMALE MUMMY FROM CHIHUAHUA, MEXICO

Stephen A. Miller

The scanning electron microscope (SEM) is a valuable tool for the study, identification, and documentation of botanical and zoological specimens. Used as a camera, the SEM is capable of high resolution and great depth of field. The SEM emphasizes surface topography; therefore, it complements other analytical and microscopic techniques.

The SEM itself consists of a high-vacuum chamber containing an elaborate electron gun and a mechanism for supporting and moving the specimen. As typically used, the electron gun produces a beam of electrons which converges to a sharp focus on the specimen and which scans a rectangular area of variable size. Secondary electrons are emitted from the specimen at the point of impact of the beam and the current of secondaries is amplified and used to modulate the intensity of a cathode-ray tube (CRT) which scans in synchrony with the SEM beam. The image thus formed on the CRT records the variations in secondary electron emission efficiency over the surface of the specimen. These variations depend mainly on the surface topography of the specimen. The CRT image is simply photographed with an ordinary camera.

For this study, samples were attached to standard aluminum mounts using a graphite suspension (Pella DAG-154). Most of the specimens were nonconductive and were therefore coated with gold (sputtered for about two minutes at 150 microns pressure and 10 milliamperes current) or with a conducting aerosol spray (Pelco Polaron spray). Without coating, the nonconductive specimens exhibit charging which results in distorted contrast and reduced resolution in the SEM image.

Specimens of potential anthropological and botanical interest were selected from the adolescent female mummy from Chihuahua, Mexico. Figures 1 and 2 show a cut, transverse section of a bit of woody fiber found in, but different from, the mummy's string skirt. This specimen is presumed to have come from the woven mat which originally wrapped the mummy. A preliminary identification suggests that it is the common cane, *Phragmites australis*, but final identification must await the availability of a suitably dried botanical specimen for comparison.

The mummy's skirt (Figure 3) is made of strings (Figure 4) composed of fibers which are twisted, flat, ribbon-like, and cohesive (Figures 5 and 6). The transverse sections show mostly homogeneous interiors, but occasionally an intricately convoluted interior is found (Figure 7). This specimen closely resembles a species of *Apocynum* (Indian hemp or dogbane).

The mummy wears anklets (Figure 8) made of fine string (Figure 9). The individual fibers have a "collapsed" section (Figures 10 and 11) characteristic of cotton. Although native species of *Gossypium* exist in the region, archaeological or ethnographic evidence of their use for fiber by the Tarahumara of the area is not mentioned by Pennington (1963); there is, however, archaeological evidence for use of cotton to the south, near the Río Zape (Brooks et al. 1962).

The final fiber specimen to be studied is from the mummy's twisted hair-foundation (Figure 12). Figures 13 and 14 show a transverse section. Figures 15-17 show the ribbed surface of the fiber with its delicately interdigitated structures bordering the ribs. These structures and the fine sawtooth border (Figure 18) are characteristic of the genus *Nolina*, and comparisons with specimens from the San Diego Museum of Natural History and the Rancho Santa Ana Botanical Garden show distinct differences from southern California species. Pennington (1963:201) records the use of *Nolina durangensis* and *N. matapensis* by the Tarahumara of the area of the mummy's origin. *N. microcarpa* may also extend into that area, but no specimen was available for comparison. Modern Tarahumara baskets in the San Diego Museum of Man are made of fibers indistinguishable from this specimen.

It is clear that only the most preliminary results are available from the SEM study reported here. Further comparative work must be done to establish the botanical identification of most of the specimens; however, as Wright (this volume) has observed, the rarity of such a specimen mandates its careful conservation. The techniques used in this study permit the documentation for comparative purposes of the smallest of specimens.

ACKNOWLEDGMENTS

I would like to acknowledge the assistance of Neil M. Davis for advice on SEM techniques; and Reid Moran of the San Diego Natural History Museum for the use of the herbarium specimens.

REFERENCES CITED

Brooks, Richard H.; Lawrence Kaplan; Hugh C. Cutler; and Thomas W. Whitaker
    1962   Plant Material from a Cave on the Rio Zape, Durango, Mexico. American Antiquity 27(3):356-369.

Pennington, Campbell W.
    1963   The Tarahumar of Mexico: Their Environment and Material Culture. Salt Lake City: University of Utah Press.

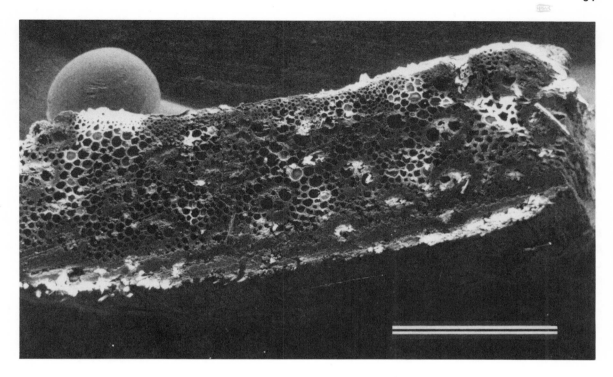

Figure 1. Transverse section of fiber from mat
(scale equals 1,000 microns).

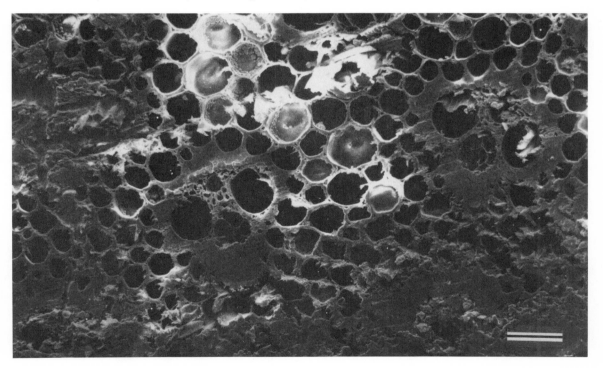

Figure 2. Detail of Figure 1
(scale equals 100 microns).

Figure 3. Close-up of string skirt
(cord diameters vary from 1.5 mm to 3 mm).

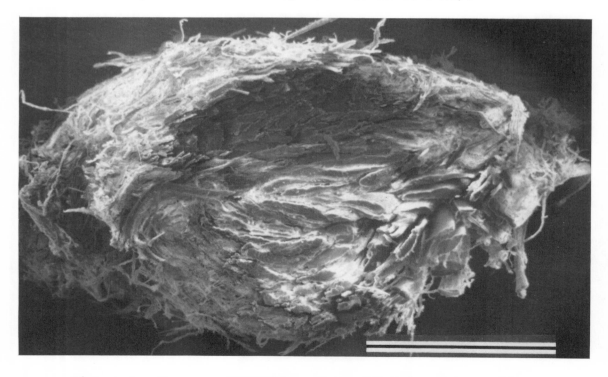

Figure 4. Transverse section of a string from the skirt
(scale equals 1,000 microns).

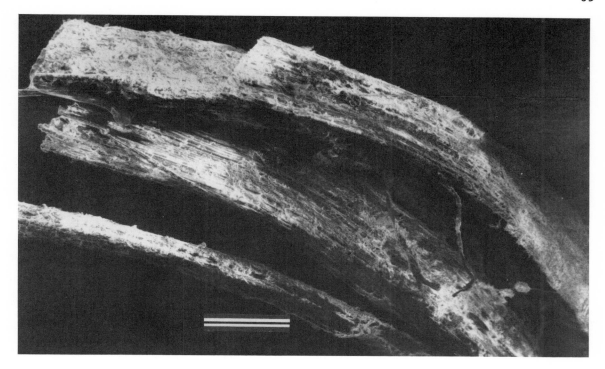

Figure 5. Lateral view of fibers within a string
(scale equals 100 microns).

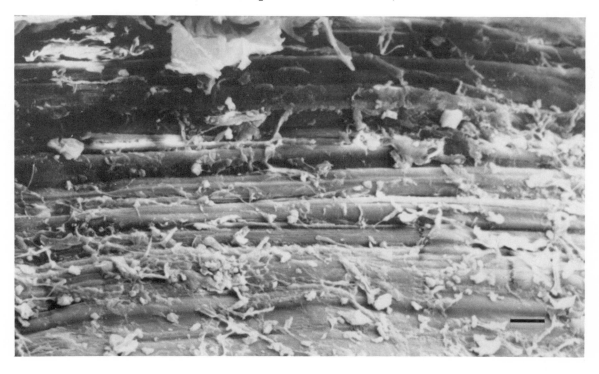

Figure 6. Detail of Figure 5
(scale equals 10 microns).

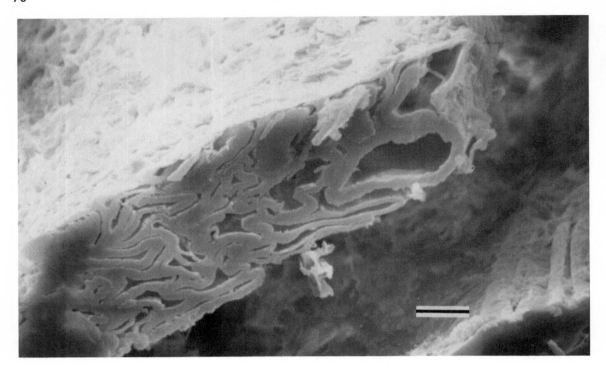

Figure 7. Transverse section of fiber showing convolutions
(scale equals 10 microns).

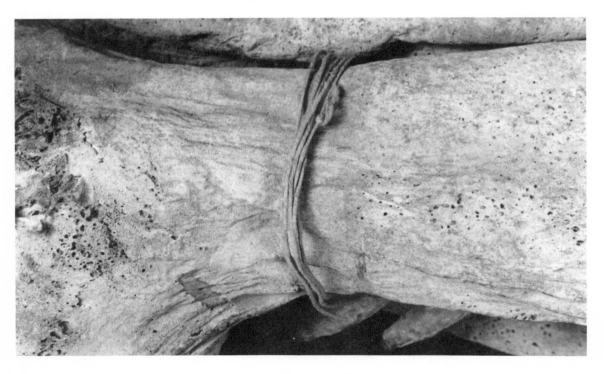

Figure 8. String anklet
(string diameter approximately 1 mm).

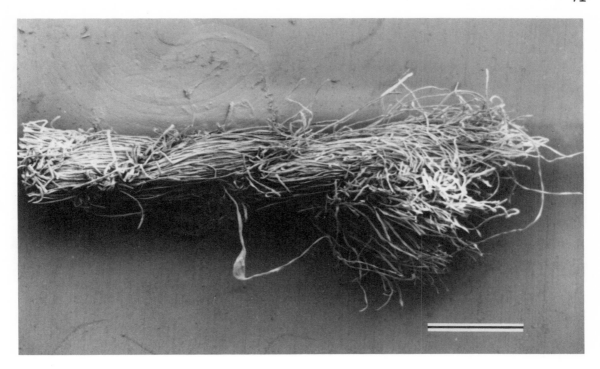

Figure 9. String from anklet
(scale equals 1,000 microns).

Figure 10. Transverse section of fibers in anklet string
(scale equals 100 microns).

72

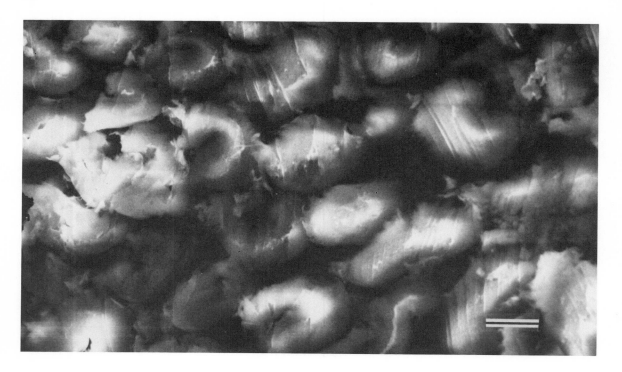

Figure 11.   Transverse section of anklet at high magnification
(scale equals 10 microns).

Figure 12.   Detail of hair-foundation
(diameter of single ply is approximately 6 mm).

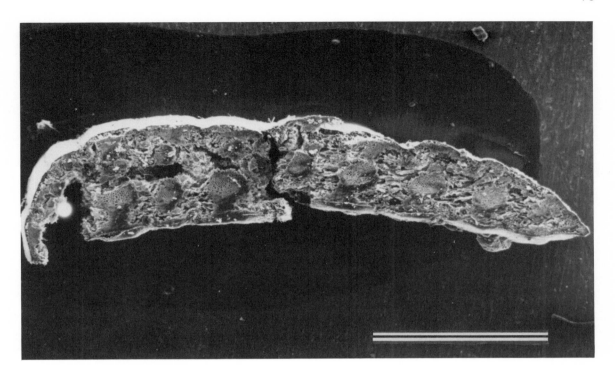

Figure 13. Tranverse section of hair-foundation fiber
(scale equals 1,000 microns).

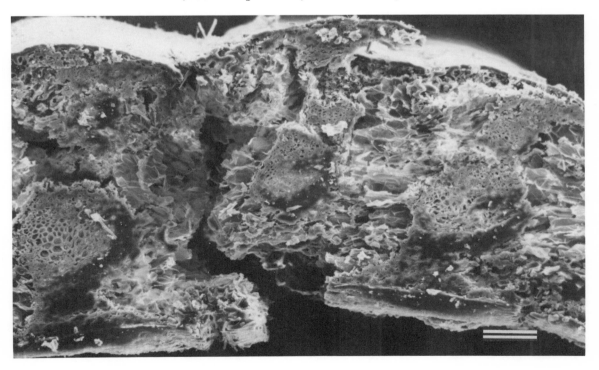

Figure 14. Detail of Figure 13
(scale equals 100 microns).

Figure 15.   Oblique view of fiber from hairband
(scale equals 1,000 microns).

Figure 16.   Detail of Figure 15
(scale equals 100 microns).

Figure 17. Detail of Figure 16
(scale equals 10 microns).

Figure 18. Sawtooth border of fiber
(scale equals 100 microns).

MEDICINAL PLANTS
OF THE TARAHUMARA INDIANS
OF CHIHUAHUA, MEXICO

Robert A. Bye, Jr.

INTRODUCTION

Plants form a large portion of the medicines ("owáame")[1] used in curing by the Tarahumara of the temperate forests of the sierras and the subtropical barrancas of southwestern Chihuahua, Mexico (Figure 1). Humans, as well as crop plants and domesticated animals, are cured in order to maintain a healthy state. To appreciate the broad application of medicinal plants, we should be aware of the Tarahumara's concept of health.

In order to present a summary of Tarahumara health, I would like to draw upon the most recent and best oriented studies on Tarahumara world view (Merrill 1978, 1981, 1983). Although these general points are based upon one community, many of the ideas have been observed by other investigators throughout the Tarahumara area. The basic outline follows Merrill's presentation of the Tarahumara conceptualization of health: their ailments, cures, and practitioners. In addition, modifications and plant examples have been derived from other sources including Anzures y Bolaños (1978, 1979); Basauri (1929); Bennett and Zingg (1935); Bye (1971-1982, 1976, 1979, in press); Bye, Burgess, and Mares (1975); Bye and Merrill (1981); García Manzanedo (1963); Irigoyen Rascón (1974, 1977); Kennedy (1970, 1978); Lumholtz (1902); Palmer (in Gray 1886; in Watson 1886); Passin (1942); Pennington (1963, 1973); Plancarte (1954); Thord-Gray (1955); and Zingg (1932). Also, the specifics of the concepts may not be applicable to all Tarahumara communities today or in the past. Certain changes such as the common use of aspirin, less consulting with native curers, and more frequent visits to institutionalized Western medical facilities have been documented among the Tarahumara who have ready access to the railroad and major roads (Llaguno 1971).

HEALTH

According to the Tarahumara, a healthy person is one whose souls are content in the body and are unharmed when they return to it. The Tarahumara health practices of perpetuating and restoring good health are based upon the condition of the souls and their relationships to the body. Certain ailments affect primarily the body and as such do not pose any serious threat unless they make the house of the souls—the body—an unpleasant place to live. Other ailments affect primarily the souls and therefore are considered to be serious.

78

Figure 1.   Chihuahua, Mexico.

The many kinds of ailments can be grouped into those which are not caused by other beings and those which are caused by other beings.[2] The former category includes things which people do to themselves and thus create circumstances under which an illness develops. Consumption of bitter items, of green corn, or of food on an empty stomach may be a cause included in this category. Certain malfunctions of the body such as a complicated childbirth and a lengthy "rumagá" (white thread that projects from the crown of a human) also belong here. These ailments are often manifested by such symptoms as loss of appetite, swollen legs, diarrhea, and gastrointestinal problems.

Other ailments are intentionally caused by other beings. One's state of health depends upon the nature of his relationship with other beings in his world. In general, four classes of beings are recognized: special plants, God, Devil, and "sukurúame."

The four types of special beings associated with plants can be placed in two subcategories. One subcategory includes those which are of no help to the Tarahumara but may cause harm to them if mistreated.

They include "uchurí" (*Echinocereus* spp. and other cacti) and "rikúhuri" (*Datura* spp.). The other subcategory includes plants which, if properly treated and periodically fed at fiestas, help and protect the individual responsible for their care. These can cause harm if mistreated, however. The Tarahumara and the plant beings are involved in a delicate reciprocal balance. These beings are associated with "híkuri" or peyote (*Lophophora williamsii* and other cacti), and the plant named "bakanawa" (Bennett and Zingg 1935:136,295) or "bakánawi" (usually identified as a cactus, but cf. *Scirpus*, Table 2, page 91; see also Merrill 1983:303).

God is a being with whom the Tarahumara also maintain a reciprocal balance. He helps and protects the Tarahumara, who must feed Him at fiestas and must behave in a beautiful fashion. If He is not treated accordingly, He may withhold His protection and even send the Devil to cause illness. If not pleased, He will also take the souls of Tarahumara children or animals, resulting in their deaths.

The Devil and his subordinates are adversaries of the Tarahumara. If placated, the Devil or his companions may not harm individuals. This may be accomplished with offerings of food or worthless gifts buried at the foot of a small cross during fiestas. The Devil controls "nawirí," forms of fogs or winds, manifested in the human body as head colds, measles, and scarlet fever. He, along with his cohorts such as coyotes, water people, magical birds, serpents, worms, and evil sorcerers, can capture or kill souls of Tarahumara dreamers.

"Sukurúame" or sorcerer carries at least three different meanings. In our brief discussion, two are of interest. One type may refer to a Tarahumara who has knowledge based upon a relationship with God or with the Devil and hence is considered to have the ability to cause and cure certain kinds of ailments that are usually associated with the soul. He may be considered good or evil depending upon how his power is practiced. The other "sukurúame" is definitely evil, causes harm and illness to the Tarahumara, and is contrasted with Tarahumara terms for curer ("rimérike," "rotóri," and "owirúame").

TREATMENT AND RITUAL

Health treatment can be classified into two categories: preventive treatment and alleviative treatment. Both may be carried out by the individual or by a native medical practitioner, depending upon the cause of the ailment.

Preventive treatments usually are ceremonial in nature. At certain fiestas, an individual may bury offerings at the base of the small "nawirí" cross for the Devil in order to avoid disease. Also one may use chile (*Capsicum annuum*) and spiny plants, such as prickly-pear cactus (*Opuntia* spp.) and acacia (*Acacia* spp.), at entrances to buildings and around *tesgüino* pots to foil sorcerers and evil beings. Specialized medical practioners during certain ceremonies employ "owáame" or medicine which is sprinkled, anointed, or sipped. This is done for protection from lightning and from contamination of food and beverage by evil, and to give one strength. Domesticated plants and animals also receive these kinds of medicines. A decoction of "mesagori" or "mé" (*Agave* spp.) and/or *tesgüino*--fermented maize (*Zea mays*) beverage--are often the most important medicines. On some occasions, colorful plants (such as the red bark of "ropogá," *Alnus* spp.) or aromatic plants (such as "wa'sía," *Ligusticum porteri*, and "wa'á," *Cupressus arizonica*) are employed.

Alleviative treatment is used when one has succumbed to an illness. The first step is to diagnose the symptoms and to review the activities of the patient and the events associated with his life. Then the cause of the ailment is determined and treatment follows. If the illness is thought to be a type of "nawirí," self-treatment or help from a non-specialist may be taken since these kinds of ailments do not require specialized knowledge and ritual to be cured. If the ailment is more serious, specialized medical practitioners may be consulted and their treatment requested. In some cases, Mexican curers and Western medical doctors may be visited since the Tarahumara believe they are creatures of the Devil, and thus have the power to cure illnesses associated with him.

There are different kinds of people involved in curing and each has his own strengths, responsibilities, and reputations. "Owirúame" is the general term applied to the curer or native medical practitioner. Each curer may have his specialty in terms of ailments treated and beings with which he interacts. An apprentice is referred to as "owéame." The "owirúame" with high reputations as curers to protect people and crops tend to devote much of their time to such activities. They usually do not cultivate but live from the offerings and payments received from the ceremonies. Such occupational specialization in a subsistence agricultural economy is considered unusual (Kennedy 1978).

The "owirúame" with his powers is able to communicate with other beings in the Tarahumara world. He often may have to retrieve lost souls to cure an individual. Also, his administration of remedies in the curing ceremonies is required if the medicinal plants are to be effective.

Other people involved in the curing include the "sukurúame," as mentioned above, and the "sawéame," with his chants and rattles. The participation of the "sawéame" is particularly important in the "tutuguri" and "yúmari" dances.

Ritual is an integral part of the practical affairs of the Tarahumara. During ceremonial curings, the medicines usually are placed under the altar or near the three main crosses (Merrill 1983:Figure 4; Kennedy 1978; and Plates 85-90 in the 1976 edition of Bennett and Zingg 1935). Various plants are involved in the curing fiestas. Some are offered and later consumed, while others are dispersed as powders, incense, or liquids on the people, fields, and animals.

The foods derived from maize (*Zea mays*), such as "sugí" (*tesgüino*), "kobisi" (*pinole*), and "ke'orí" (*esquiate*), are usually present at the ceremonies. Occasionally, other food plants may include "pachí" (green maize) and "muní" (beans) (*Phaseolus vulgaris*, *P. coccineus*). *Tesgüino* is consumed not only as food, but also for its curative properties. Many plants (Table 1) are added to the cooked, ground corn during fermentation and are said to aid in *tesgüino* production and to provide curative effects. The fermentation is a closed batch process (Litzinger 1983) which may be influenced by various outside factors. Biological functions of the *tesgüino* additives in the fermentation process as well as in the Tarahumara consumer are not understood. Many of the plants are known to contain antimicrobial substances which may decrease certain microorganisms.

Leaves and roasted hearts of magueys (*Agave* spp.) are used variously in Tarahumara ceremonies. "Mesagori" or "ojkome" (*Agave wocomahi*) appears to be the most important in ceremonies. An infusion of the midsection of the leaves is almost always present at such occasions in the sierras. Leaves of "sokó" (*Yucca* spp.) are sometimes employed as well. The pungent fruits of "korí sívre" (*Capsicum annuum* var. *glabriusculum*) from the barrancas are commonly used as a powder, either dry or mixed with water. The dried pulverized bark of trees such as "uré" (*Fraxinus* spp.) and "ropogá" (*Alnus* spp.) is occasionally employed, especially for curing animals. The aromatic branches of "wa'á" (*Cupressus arizonica*) and less commonly "awarí" (*Juniperus* spp., especially *J. deppeana*) are used in various parts of a curing process and sweatbaths. The strong smelling woods of "matowi" (*Buddleia cordata*) and "chopé" or pitchpine (resin-rich split wood from girdled pines of the *Pinus ponderosa* group) are employed in many ceremonies. The highly prized "morewá" is derived from the nests of solitary wasps that build under rock shelves in the barrancas. The wasps gather the exudates from wounds (often made by the Tarahumara) on *torote* (*Bursera* spp.). Other incense plants include the bark of "iwíchuri" (*Hintonia latiflora*) and the herbs of the pungent smelling "rochíwari" (*Lepidium* sp.). Smoking tobacco during ceremonies is very important. Although commercial tobacco is used, local tobaccos such as the cultivated "wipá" (*Nicotiana rustica* and *N. tabacum*) or the wild "iwará" (*N. trigonophylla*) are preferred.

Many other plants, which may be consumed by the participants in the ceremony and/or by the patient, are part of the rituals. Some are administered to the patients (see Table 2); others provide materials for construction of altars, crosses, instruments, vessels, and decorations. Those used as construction material are not considered in this paper.

The data on role and use of the plants referred to as "uchurí," "rikúhuri," "híkuri," and "bakánawi" are little known, inconsistent, and sometimes conflicting, depending upon the observer. In general, they are not handled by all the Tarahumara but rather by a few specialists. Any interaction with them is always associated with ritual. The effects of these plants can be produced by a person's consumption or application as well as by the presence of the beings represented by the plants.

MEDICINAL PLANTS

While many of the above plants are used as medicines in a ceremonial context, they, along with other plants, are administered in self-medication or home treatment. Nearly 300 botanical species of these plants are listed in Table 2. The data on these plants were derived from my collections of specimens and data and/or observations as well as from literature and unpublished sources. Citations of the data from other sources are separate because it was not possible to verify the identification of the plants.

Table 1

Plants Added to Tarahumara *Tesgüino**

LICHENS

Usneaceae
  Usnea subusca
  Usnea variolosa
  Usnea sp.

FERN AND FERN-ALLIES

Polypodiaceae
  Polypodium aureum
  Polypodium erythrolepis
  Polypodium polypodioides
  Polypodium sp.

Selaginellaceae
  Selaginella cuspidata
  Selaginella lepidophylla
  Selaginella pilifera

FLOWERING PLANTS

Cactaceae (possibly other genera;
    see Bye 1979)
  Ariocarpus fissuratus
  Lophophora williamsii
  Pachycereus pecten-aboriginum

Compositae (plus some
    unidentified plants)
  Hieracium fendleri
  Stevia serrata
  Stevia sp.
  Tagetes sp.

Cyperaceae
  Fimbristylis sp.
  Scirpus sp.

Garryaceae
  Garrya wrightii

Gramineae
  Bromus arizonicus
  Bromus porteri

Labiatae
  Agastache spp. (including
      Brittonastrum spp.)
  Hyptis sp.
  Mentha spp.
  Monarda austromontana

Leguminosae
  Acacia sp.
  Phaseolus metcalfei
  Phaseolus sp.

Malvaceae
  Abelmoschus sp.

Plumbaginaceae
  Plumbago scandens

Pyrolaceae
  Chimaphila dasystemma
  Chimaphila maculata

Rubiaceae
  Hintonia latiflora (including
      Coutarea pterosperma)
  Randia echinocarpa
  Randia laevigata
  Randia watsoni

Scrophulariaceae
  Penstemon cf. *campanulatus*

Solanaceae (possibly other
    species; see Bye 1979)
  Datura inoxia

*from Bennett and Zingg (1935), Bye (1971-1982, 1976), Litzinger (1982),
  Merrill (1978, 1981), and Pennington (1963).

The plant parts used, the form of preparation/administration, and the ailment treated are presented for each plant in code form (see Key to Table 2). The ailment categories are generalized because the information was obtained with the Spanish terms approximating the symptoms. The specific Tarahumara illness categories were not obtained. Because there are basic differences in terms of concept, diagnosis, etiology, and treatment between Tarahumara illnesses and illnesses from the viewpoint of the Western scientific community, it is not worthwhile to compare their attributes specifically. The generalization given in Table 2 provides a context for describing the employment of these medicinal plants. An evaluation of their effectiveness from the Tarahumara viewpoint, following the cultural approach elaborated by Ortiz de Montellano (1975), or from the Western chemo-pharmacological viewpoint is also inappropriate at this time. As pointed out in another paper (Bye, in press), little is known about the biology, phytochemistry, and pharmacology of the plants from this region.

The Tarahumara generally collect medicinal plants from specific areas and from specific plant populations. In some cases, these plants are found in fields and disturbed habitats; as anthropogenic annuals or short-lived perennials, they are what we consider to be weeds. Other plants grow wild in areas away from the dwellings and cultivated fields. Some plants are collected, dried, and stored for future use. Often one sees various herbs and roots suspended from the roof or wedged in wall crevices. Others are gathered fresh from nearby areas when needed. Certain plants require a special trip to be obtained. In addition, some plants may not be readily available or their location may be unknown to the person needing them. These may be obtained through trade or purchase from other Tarahumara Indians who carry out inter-regional trade throughout the sierras and the barrancas.

The Tarahumara do not seem to show a possessive attitude about plants unless they are planted. A person who is not the owner of a cultivated plant may not exploit it except in the case of emergency or with the permission of the owner. The wild and weedy plants of the field and forest, on the other hand, may be gathered by anyone as long as he respects the plant, gathers it correctly and at the appropriate time, and obtains only what he needs.

Despite the openness of this system for obtaining plant material, the Tarahumara tend to be restrictive in their exploitation of vegetal resources. On one occasion, I went collecting "matarique" (*Psacalium* [= *Odontotrichum*] *decompositum*) with an elderly Tarahumara in the Gonogochi region, and even though we passed many stands of the perennial herb during the trip, he insisted that the medicine came from a population farther down the trail. Botanically, these plants were the same species and had the same Tarahumara name as the medicinal plants we later collected. On another occasion, an elderly Tarahumara from Cusarare accompanied me on a trip to the barranca of the Río Urique to the south. He was able to give me the names of many plants but indicated that he did not know their properties. Even though they were the same botanical species and he said they looked like the same curative plants as those near his house, he could not say if these were medicinal. The popular "korí sívre" (*Capsicum annuum* var. *glabriusculum*) is a wild and anthropogenic shrub in the barranca. One year, there was a great demand for the wild peppers in the sierras due to a large number of road construction people. The price was high enough to encourage some Tarahumara workers and their mestizo companions to go to the Barranca de Batopilas. They carelessly picked the peppers, often damaging or uprooting the shrubs. The Tarahumara Indians from that region of the barranca considered this situation to be wrong and, after a slightly violent altercation, forced the intruders back to the sierras. These incidents suggest that the Tarahumara consider certain plants from certain areas to be special, and that these need to be respected. The bases for these attributes are many and complex.

ENDNOTES

1. The Tarahumara terms used in this paper are written as they appeared in the various references and unpublished materials with the exception of č and š, which have been changed to ch and sh, respectively. In order to provide some consistency, certain words are based upon those listed in Brambila's (1976) recent Tarahumara dictionary. Tarahumara words are shown in quotation marks rather than the conventional italics.

2. García M. (1963) divides diseases into natural ones (e.g., "ripiwirî," "risagî," and "rurusî") and supernatural ones (e.g., "majárike," "rusîware," and "korimaka"). Based upon their characteristics, they all appear to be related to the subcategory of illnesses caused by other beings.

ACKNOWLEDGMENTS

I would like to acknowledge the hospitality and field assistance extended to me over the years by L. G. Verplancken, S.J.; J. Candler; and D. Burgess. C. W. Pennington and W. L. Merrill have provided constant stimulation with their critical comments on my view of the world which we explore periodically in the Sierra Tarahumara. Finally, my sincerest thanks to to the "Rarámuri," the Tarahumara people, who have shared a part of their world with this "chabochi."

Financial support over the years during which much of these data were gathered was provided by Harvard University (Botanical Museum and Department of Biology), University of Colorado (Department of Environmental, Population and Organismic Biology, University Museum and Council on Research and Creative Work), National Geographic Society, and National Science Foundation (GB-35047).

REFERENCES CITED

Anzures y Bolaños, C.
  1978   Medicina Tradicional entre los Tarahumaras. Revista Medicina
          Tradicional 1(4):39-47.

  1979   La Relacion Medico-Paciente en la Sierra Tarahumara. In C.
          Viesca Trevino, ed. Estudios sobre Etnobotánica y Anthro-
          pología Medica, III, pp. 59-71. México, D.F.: Instituto
          Mexicano para el Estudio de las Plantas Medicinales, A.C.

Basauri, C.
  1929   Monografía de los Tarahumaras. México, D.F.: Talleres
          Gráficos de la Nación.

Bennett, W. C., and R. M. Zingg
  1935   The Tarahumara: An Indian Tribe of Northern Mexico. Chicago:
          University of Chicago Press. (New edition with color photo-
          graphs by L. G. Verplancken, S.J., published by Rio Grande
          Press, Inc., Glorieta, New Mexico, 1976).

Brambila, D.
  1976   Diccionario Rarámuri-Castellano (Tarahumar). México, D.F.:
          La Obra Nacional de la Buena Prensa, A.C.

Bye, R. A., Jr.
  1971-   Botanical Field Notes Taken While Conducting Ethnobotanical
  1982   and Floristic Studies in the Sierra Madre Occidental of
          Southwestern Chihuahua, Mexico. Manuscripts in possession of
          R. Bye. Specimens deposited at Harvard University,
          Universidad Nacional Autónoma de México, University of
          Colorado, and other herbaria.

  1976   The Ethnoecology of the Tarahumara of Chihuahua, Mexico.
          Unpublished Ph.D. Thesis (Biology), Harvard University,
          Cambridge, Massachusetts.

  1979   Hallucinogenic Plants of the Tarahumara. Journal of
          Ethnopharmacology 1(1):23-48.

  in   Medicinal Plants of the Sierra Madre: A Comparative Study of
  press   Tarahumara and Mexican Market Plants. Economic Botany.

Bye, R. A., Jr.; D. Burgess; and A. Mares Trías
  1975   Ethnobotany of the Western Tarahumara of Chihuahua, Mexico.
          I. Notes on the Genus *Agave*. Harvard University, Botanical
          Museum Leaflets 24(5):85-112.

Bye, R. A., Jr., and W. L. Merrill
    1981   Medicinal Plants of the Sierra Madre: A Comparative Study of
            Tarahumara and Mexican Market Plants. Paper presented at the
            annual meeting of the American Anthropological Association,
            Los Angeles, California, in the Symposium "Herbalism in
            Latin America: Multidisciplinary Perspectives."

García Manzanedo, H.
    1963   Notas Sobre la Medicina Tradicional en Una Zona de la Sierra
            Tarahumara. América Indígena 23(1):61-70.

Gray, A.
    1886   Contributions to American Botany. 2. Sertum Chihuahuense.
            Proceedings of the American Academy of Arts and Sciences
            21:378-409.

Irigoyen Rascón, F.
    1974   Cerocahui: Una Communidad en la Tarahumara. México, D.F.:
            Universidad Nacional Autónoma de México.

    1977   Cha Okó! (¡Me duele mucho!). México, D.F.: Obra Nacional de
            la Buena Prensa, A.C.

Kennedy, J. G.
    1970   Inápuchi: Una Communidad Tarahumara Gentil. México, D.F.:
            Instituto Indigenista Interamericano.

    1978   Tarahumara of the Sierra Madre: Beer, Ecology, and Social
            Organization. Arlington Heights, Illinois: AMH Publishing
            Corporation.

Litzinger, W. J.
    1983   The Ethnobiology of Alcoholic Beverage Production by the
            Lacandon, Tarahumara, and other Aboriginal Mesoamerican
            Peoples. Unpublished Ph.D. Dissertation, University of
            Colorado, Boulder.

Llaguno, R. J.
    1971   Change in the Tarahumara Family: The Influence of the
            Railroad. Unpublished M.A. Thesis, Department of Sociology,
            Louisiana State University, Baton Rouge.

Lumholtz, C.
    1902   Unknown Mexico: A Record of Five Years' Exploration among
            the Tribes of the Western Sierra Madre; in the Tierra
            Caliente of Tepic and Jalisco; and among the Tarascos of
            Michoacan. Vols. I and II. New York: Charles Scribner's
            Sons.

Merrill, W. L.
    1978   Thinking and Drinking: A Rarámuri Interpretation. In: R.
            I. Ford, ed., The Nature and Status of Ethnobotany, pp. 101-
            117. University of Michigan, Museum of Anthropology,
            Anthropology Papers No. 67.

    1981   The Concept of Soul among the Rarámuri of Chihuahua, Mexico:
            A Study in World View. Unpublished Ph.D. Dissertation,
            University of Michigan, Ann Arbor.

    1983   Tarahumara Social Organization, Political Organization, and
            Religion. In: A. Ortiz, ed., Handbook of North American
            Indians, Vol. 10, pp. 290-305. Washington, D.C.:
            Smithsonian Institution.

Ortiz de Montellano, B.
    1975   Empirical Aztec Medicine. Science 188:215-220.

Passin, H.
    1942   Sorcery as a Phase of Tarahumara Economic Relations. Man
            42(1):11-15.

Pennington, C. W.
    1963   The Tarahumar of Mexico: Their Environment and Material
            Culture. Salt Lake City: University of Utah Press.

    1973   Plantas Medicinales Utilizadas por los Tarahumara.
            Chihuahua, Chih.: Imprenta Esparza.

Plancarte, F. M.
    1954   El Problema Indígena Tarahumara. Memorias del Instituto
            Nacional Indigenista, Vol. V. México, D.F.: Instituto
            Nacional Indigenista.

Thord-Gray, I.
    1955   Tarahumara-English, English-Tarahumara Dictionary and an
            Introduction to Tarahumara Grammar. Coral Gables, Florida:
            University of Miami Press.

Watson, S.
    1886   Contributions to American Botany. 1. List of Plants
            Collected by Dr. Edward Palmer in Southwestern Chihuahua,
            Mexico, in 1885. Proceedings of the American Academy of Arts
            and Sciences 21:414-445.

Zingg, R. M.
    1932   Mexican Folk Remedies of Chihuahua, Mexico. Journal of the
            Washington Academy of Sciences 22:174-181.

Key to Table 2. Tarahumara Medicinal Plants

The utilization code is listed in the 4 columns at the right of the table: Plant Part Used, Form of Administration, Ailment Treated, and Source. The underlined code indicates that the use is primarily for animals. The code enclosed in slashes (//) denotes that the plant part is a result of plant-animal interaction (e.g. gum exudate). An asterisk (*) indicates that the botanical determination is different from that given in the original source; for corresponding plant names from the literature, see Table 3, page 104. Parentheses around botanical names ( ) indicate uncertain identification. A plus symbol (+) indicates a name in Mexican Spanish.

PLANT PART:

b	=	bark	ts	=	*tesgüino*	
e	=	exudate	vp	=	vapor inhaled	
fl	=	flowers	w	=	wash, lotion from	
fr	=	fruits			hot decoction	
fs	=	flowerstalk				
i	=	immature part, as				
		indicated				
j	=	juice				
l	=	leaves				
lt	=	latex				
r	=	root				
rs	=	resin				
s	=	stem				
sd	=	seed				
sp	=	spines				
w	=	whole plant, above				
		ground				
wd	=	wood				

AILMENT TREATED:

he = heart ailments
     (weak, irregular
     palpitation)
hp = hunger pains
ht = heat prostration
if = inflammations
in = insecticide
j = jaundice
k = kidney ailments
l = liver ailments
lg = lung, pulmonary ailments
m = medicine, general
ml = malaria
mn = menstrual pains
mp = measles and pox
mu = muscle relaxant
n = nausea
ns = nasal congestion
p = purgative, laxative,
     cathartic
pa = pains or aches, general
pai = pain, internal
pb = purify blood
pn = pneumonia
pr = pregnancy & conception,
      aid in
py = paralysis
r = rheumatism
rs = rashes, itches
s = sores, cankers
sl = sleep, aid in
sp = sprains
st = stomach infections,
     gastric ulcers
sw = swellings
t = teeth & gums, improvement
ta = toothaches, sore gums
th = throat, sore, catarrh
to = tonic, general medicinal
u = urinary ailments
ul = ulcers
v = vermifuge
ve = veneral diseases
vm = vomiting, emetic
wc = wash clothes
wd = wounds, cuts, scratches,
     surface infections
wt = weight (to lose)

FORM OF ADMINISTRATION:

a = alcohol beverage,
     infusion in
ap = application,
      insertion
b = bath
bo = boiled
c = crushed, powder
cn = cane, carried
cs = cast
e = eaten
en = enema
f = fermented beverage
i = infusion (soak in
     cold water)
in = incense
j = juice, plant sap
m = masticate
mix = mixture of different
      plants
o = ointment, salve
p = poultice
r = raw, eaten
s = *sotol* drink
sb = sweat bath
sm = smoke
sn = snuff
t = tea (hot decoction
     or infusion)

AILMENT TREATED:

ab = abortifacient
ag = astringent
an = anesthetic, topical
as = asthma
at = antihelminthic,
      topical
b = bruises
ba = bladder ailments
bb = broken bones
bk = back ailments & pain
bl = boils
bp = body pain, general
br = bad breath
bt = bites, poisonous
bu = burns
c = colds, flu
cb = childbirth
cc = chest congestion,
      bronchial inflam-
      mation, chest pains
ch = chills
cl = colic
cn = constipation
co = coughs
cu = "curing," general &
      preventative
d = diabetes
dr = diarrhea
dy = dysentery
er = ear ailment, aches,
      noises
ey = eye infections,
      ailments
f = fever
fr = fright
ft = foot infections
gi = gastrointestinal ail-
      ments, indigestion,
      pain, stomach aches,
      gas
h = hair, scalp wash
hd = headaches

SOURCES:

BYE = Collections of the author
BZ = Bennett & Zingg (1935)
H = Hewitt (specimens at Gray Herbarium)
I = Irigoyen Rascon (1974)
L = Lumholtz expedition (Lumholtz 1902; Lumholtz & Hartman, specimens at Gray Herbarium)
PM = Palmer (specimens at Gray Herbarium and unpublished notes)
PN = Pennington (1963)

Table 2

Tarahumara Medicinal Plants

Botanical Name	Native Name	Plant Part	Form of Admin.	Ailment Treated	Source
LICHENS					
USNEACEAE					
Parmelia caperata	ŕeté cajéra	w	c	bu	PN
Usnea sp.	riteawáare	w	t	cb	BYE
BRYOPHYTA					
Undetermined	re'eke buwara	w	w	hd	BYE
PTERIDOPHYTA					
EQUISETACEAE					
Equisetum laevigatum	kawasíola	w	w	wd	BYE
Equisetum laevigatum	bakushi	s	t	cc	PN
Equisetum hyemale var. *affine*	pakuchara	w	t	u	BYE
POLYPODIACEAE					
Adiantum capillus-veneris	muchukaka	w	t	he	BYE
Asplenium monanthes	muchogaka	w	t	he	BYE
Cheilanthes pyramidalis	mochogaka	w	t	cc,gi,he	BYE
*Cheilanthes pyramidalis**	wichasuwa	l	t	lg	PN
Cheilanthes tomentosa	machogá	s,l	t	u	PN
Dryopteris normalis	machogá	r	c,t	mn	PN
Dryopteris normalis		r	c,p	bk	PN
Notholaena aurea	kalawala	w	t	cc,k,he	BYE
Notholaena candida	kanawála		t	f	BZ
Notholaena candida		w	t	k	PM
Notholaena limitanea	kalawala	w	t	co,l	BYE
Pellaea ternifolia var. *wrightii*	pívora	w	t	cc,he	BYE
Pteridium aquilinum var. *pubescens*	machogaka	r	t	m	BYE
Woodsia mexicana	wachigónuri	l	t	bp	PN
Woodsia mexicana		l	c,p	r	PN
Woodwardia spinulosa	ma'sagá	l		cu	BYE
SELAGINELLACEAE					
Selaginella pilifera var. *pringlei*		w	t	m	BYE
CONIFERAE					
CUPRESSACEAE					
Cupressus arizonica	wa'á	l	sb	m,cu	BYE

Botanical Name	Native Name	Plant Part	Form of Admin.	Ailment Treated	Source
Cupressus arizonica	wa'á	l	t	c,co,hd	BYE
Cupressus arizonica		l	vp,in	cu	BYE
Cupressus arizonica	waá	l	t	co	PN
Juniperus deppeana	awarí	l	t	c,co,bp, gi,m,th	BYE
Juniperus deppeana		l	w	m,r	BYE
Juniperus deppeana		l	vp,in	cu	BYE
Juniperus deppeana*	aorí, aborí, awarí, kawarí, koarí	l	b	mu	PN
Juniperus deppeana*		l	t	co	PN
Juniperus deppeana*		l	sb	cu,m	PN
Juniperus deppeana		wd		cu	L
Juniperus durangensis	péchuri	l	t	co	BYE
Juniperus durangensis		l	vp	cu,m	BYE
(Juniperus mexicana)	waáka	l	sb	f,pa,cu	BZ
(Juniperus mexicana)	aworíki	l	bo,w	mu	BZ
PINACEAE					
Pinus ayacahuite	wiyoko	rs	t	co,m	BYE
Pinus ayacahuite		rs	p	br	BYE
Pinus ayacahuite		rs	o	ft	BYE
Pinus ayacahuite	wiyó	l	t	co	PN
Pinus ayacahuite		rs	o	ft	PN
Pinus ayacahuite	wiyóko	rs	o	ft	BZ
Pinus chihuahuana	sawaka	l	t	hd	BYE
Pinus lumholtzii		l	t	co	PN
Pinus lumholtzii		l	t	gi	L
Pinus reflexa	mategó, mateyó	rs	ap	r	PN
Pinus reflexa		rs	t	lg	PN
Pinus reflexa		l	t	co	PN
Pinus sp.		s,l	s	cu	BZ

ANGIOSPERMAE -- MONOCOTYLEDONES

AGAVACEAE

Botanical Name	Native Name	Plant Part	Form of Admin.	Ailment Treated	Source
Agave bovicornuta		l	j	s	PN
(Agave shrevei)	watusá		i	cu	BZ
Agave vilmoriniana	awé	l	j	h,wc	BYE
Agave wocomahi	mesagori	l	t	hd	BYE
Agave wocomahi		l	i	cu	BYE
Dasylirion durangense	seléke		i	cu	BZ
Dasylirion wheeleri	seréke	fs	p	hd	PN
Yucca schottii	sokó	l	j	h,wc	BYE
Yucca schottii*	sóko	r		h,wc	BZ

BROMELIACEAE

Botanical Name	Native Name	Plant Part	Form of Admin.	Ailment Treated	Source
Tillandsia benthamiana	dowáka sewála	w	t	p	BZ
Tillandsia karwinskyana	reteshíwara	l	t	cn	PN
Tillandsia sp.	wechíra	l	w	r	PN

CYPERACEAE

Botanical Name	Native Name	Plant Part	Form of Admin.	Ailment Treated	Source
Cyperus sp.	anarora	w	t	m	BYE
Fimbristylis sp.	kasaláka	w,r	c,t	c,pn	BZ

Botanical Name	Native Name	Plant Part	Form of Admin.	Ailment Treated	Source
Fimbristylis sp.		w	ts	c	BZ
Scirpus sp.	bakánawi	r	p	r,wd	BYE
GRAMINEAE					
Coix lacryma-jobi	rosário[+]	fr		cu	BYE
Elyonurus barbiculmis	saparike	r	t	gi,br	BYE
Elyonurus barbiculmis		r	m	ta	PM
Muhlenbergia porteri	bakú	r	bo,c,p	r,bk	PN
Panicum bulbosum	witavorachi	r	r	vm	BYE
Panicum bulbosum		r	t	th,m	BYE
*Phragmites australis**		s		cu	PN
*Phragmites australis**		fr		d,gi	I
IRIDACEAE					
Sisyrinchium arizonicum	torímasari	r,w	t	gi	BYE
Sisyrinchium sp.	ramego'nowa	r	r	ta	BYE
LILIACEAE					
Aloe barbadensis	sábila[+]	l	j	bu,s	BYE

ANGIOSPERMAE -- DICOTYLEDONES

Botanical Name	Native Name	Plant Part	Form of Admin.	Ailment Treated	Source
ACANTHACEAE					
Carlowrightia sp.	yerba de torro[+]	w	t	ml	BYE
Elytraria imbricata	kochweasira	w	t	co,lg,th	BYE
Elytraria imbricata	kirí	l	t	dr,f	PN
Elytraria imbricata		w	w	wd	PN
Elytraria imbricata		w	t	ve,ml	PM
Elytraria imbricata		w	t	k,p,gi	I
Jacobinia candicans	huachachile[+]	l	t	f	H
AMARANTHACEAE					
Alternanthera repens	witichókare	l,r	t,r	f,gi,hd, th	BYE
Alternanthera repens	nachúkurusi	l	t	gi	PN
Alternanthera repens		r	c,i	u	PN
APOCYNACEAE					
Plumeria acutifolia	rachiló	b,lt	t	p,wd	BYE
Plumeria acutifolia		r	t	p	PN
Plumeria acutifolia	dotcilóko	r	c,i	p	BZ
Stemmadenia palmeri	bírako	l	c,j	wd,s	BYE
Vallesia glabra	duduwasa	fr		m	BYE
AQUIFOLIACEAE					
Ilex rubra	curiento[+]	fr		p	H
ARALIACEAE					
Aralia humilis var. *pubescens*	kamochin	b,l	t	f	BYE
ARISTOLOCHIACEAE					
*Aristolochia wrightii**		r,s	t	gi	PN

Botanical Name	Native Name	Plant Part	Form of Admin.	Ailment Treated	Source
*Aristolochia wrightii**[*]	Santa María[+]	r	c,t	f	BZ
ASCLEPIADACEAE					
Asclepias linaria	patito[+]	l	j	p,s,wd	BYE
Asclepias tuberosa	inmortal[+]	s	c,sn	ns	PN
Asclepias sp.	escoranilla[+]	r	t	m	BYE
Asclepias sp.	chiwainame, nakáka	l	c,p	r	PN
Asclepias sp.	tcomalínakala	r	c,t	p	BZ
Asclepias sp.				ve	BZ
Matelea sp.	choríki	r	c,p	bl	PN
BETULACEAE					
Alnus oblongifolia	ropogá	b	i	cu	BYE
BIGNONIACEAE					
Crescentia alata		i,fr	i	c	BZ
*Tabebuia chrysantha**[*]	mapá	l,s	t	bk,lg	PN
Tecoma stans	kusí urákame	fl	t	c	PN
Tecoma stans		fl	o	he	PN
BORAGINACEAE					
Amsinckia sp.	sarabora	w	t	m	BYE
BURSERACEAE					
Bursera bipinnata	torote[+]	rs	r	bu,er,ey	BYE
Bursera bipinnata		rs	p	an	PM
Bursera grandifolia	iweri	b	t	c,hd	BYE
Bursera grandifolia	palo mulato[+]	b	bo,t	dy	BZ
Bursera grandifolia		rs	p	r	I
Bursera lancifolia	rusíwari	rs	m	t	BYE
Bursera lancifolia		rs	w,p	bu,er,ey	BYE
Bursera lancifolia		rs	p	r,an	
Bursera lancifolia		rs	m	t	PM
Bursera penicillata	torote[+]	rs		m	PM
Bursera spp.	morewá	/rs/	in	cu	BYE
Bursera spp.		/rs/	t	co,cu	BYE
CACTACEAE					
Ariocarpus fissuratus	jíkuri	w	m,p	b,bt,wd	PN
Ariocarpus fissuratus		j	i,o	r	PN
Cephalocereus sp.	pitahaya barbona[+]	w	cs	bb	I
Echinocereus sp.	napísala	w	cs	bb	BYE
Lophophora williamsii	jíkuri	w	m,p	b,bt,wd	PN
Lophophora williamsii		j	i,o	r	PN
Mammallaria heyderi	witculíki	j	ap	er	BZ
Opuntia spp.	iraka	s	p	bt,bu	BYE
Opuntia sp.	iláka	s	p	pa	BZ
Opuntia sp.	ulibecha	s	cs	bb	BYE
Pachycereus pecten-aboriginum	wichowaka	s	t	m,pa,p	BYE
CHENOPODIACEAE					
Chenopodium ambrosioides	basota	w	t	f,gi,hd, pa,r,v	BYE

Botanical Name	Native Name	Plant Part	Form of Admin.	Ailment Treated	Source
Chenopodium ambrosioides		w	w,p	at,pa,r	BYE
Chenopodium ambrosioides		l	t	f,gi	PN
Chenopodium ambrosioides		w	t	f	PM
Chenopodium ambrosioides		l	t	v	PN
Chenopodium graveolens	yerba del zorillo[+]	w	t	dr,gi	BYE
CISTACEAE					
Helianthemum glomeratum	rojáshowa	l	t	co,f	BYE
Helianthemum glomeratum	ŕojáshowa	l	i	co,f	PN
Helianthemum glomeratum	halába		t	f	BZ
COMPOSITAE					
Ambrosia acanthicarpa	u'rí	l	p	s,wd	BYE
Ambrosia ambrosioides	chikuri	l	p	sw	BYE
Ambrosia psilostachya	chipúnua	l	t	gi	BYE
Artemisia ludoviciana var. *mexicana*	rosáwari	l	t	dr,gi	BYE
Artemisia ludoviciana var. *mexicana*	ŕosábari	l	t	mn	PN
Artemisia ludoviciana var. *mexicana*		l	t	m	PM
Baccharis glutinosa	chagushi	l	c,p	s	PN
Baccharis sp.	ropagónowa	l	t	gi	BYE
Baccharis sp.	pasmo[+]	l,s	t	co,c	BZ
Baccharis sp.		l,s	bo,p	s,wd	BZ
Berlandiera lyrata var. *macrophylla*	coronilla[+]	r	t,w	gi	BYE
Berlandiera lyrata var. *macrophylla*	coronilla[+]	r	t	p	PN
Bidens pilosa	sepeke	fl	t	k	BYE
Cirsium mexicanum	chiná[+]	l	m	t	BYE
Cosmos parviflorus	kuhuve	w	t	gi,m	BYE
Cosmos pringlei	babisa[+]	r	t	gi	BYE
Cosmos pringlei	ripúraka, ripúri, wasarépuri, bavísa[+]	r	c,p	s,at	PN
Cosmos pringlei		r	t	dr	I
Cosmos pringlei		r	t	gi,hd	PN
Cosmos pringlei		r	t	gi	L
Eupatorium sp.	dulubútci	j		p	BZ
Eupatorium sp.		r	c,r	gi	BZ
Gnaphalium wrightii	rosábori	w	t	dr,gi	BYE
Gnaphalium wrightii	chiyowi, ŕasorá ŕasóko	l,fl	t	co,dr	PN
Gnaphalium sp.	rosábari	w	t	dr,gi	BYE
Gnaphalium sp.	telempakáte	fl,s	t	c	BZ
Helianthella quinquenervis	raresoa	r	w	at,h	BYE
Helianthella quinquenervis		r	t	gi,u	BYE
Hieracium fendleri	rawichi shitakame, chikuri nakara	l	c,p	s,wd	PN
Hieracium sp.	bahíname	l	ap	er,hd	BYE
Hieracium sp.	daragótci	l	c	bl,s,ul	BZ
Iostephane heterophylla	escorcionera[+]	r	p,t	br,bk,p, py	BYE
Iostephane heterophylla		r	p	bt,s,wd	PM

Botanical Name	Native Name	Plant Part	Form of Admin.	Ailment Treated	Source
Parthenium tomentosum var. stramonium	wasároa	s	ap	ta	BYE
Parthenium tomentosum var. stramonium		s,lt	w,p	r,wd	BYE
Pectis stenophylla	limoncillo[+]	w	t	hd,gi	BYE
Pectis stenophylla		l	t	u	PN
Pectis stenophylla		l	vp	c	PN
Perezia thurberi	pipichowa	r	t	n,p,to	BYE
Pionocarpus madrensis	kachana	r	t,w	r	BYE
Pionocarpus madrensis		r	ap	ta	BYE
Psacalium decompositum	matarique	r	t	bp,c,f, gi,m,r	BYE
Psacalium decompositum		r	p	r,s	BYE
Psacalium decompositum*	matariqui	l,r	t	f,ml	PN
Psacalium decompositum*		r	c,p	wd	PN
Psacalium decompositum*		r	ap	ta	PN
Psacalium decompositum*		r	c,t	r	PN
Psacalium decompositum*	pitcáwi	r	t	p	BZ
Psacalium decompositum*		w	c,bo,t	c	BZ
Psacalium decompositum*		w	c,bo,w	wd	BZ
Psacalium decompositum*		r	t	d,k	H
Psacalium decompositum*		r	w,c	r	H
Psacalium globosum	nakáruri	r	w,p	r	BYE
Ratibida mexicana	onora	r	t	gi	BYE
Ratibida mexicana		l,r	c,t	co,hd	PN
Ratibida mexicana		r	c,p	s	PN
Senecio candidissimus	chukaka	l	p,w	s,ve	BYE
Senecio candidissimus		r	ap	ta	BYE
Senecio candidissimus		l	t	ba,k	H
Senecio candidissimus		l	p,o	bl,sw	H
Senecio chapalensis	sepepare	l,j	ap	at,wd	H
Senecio hartwegii	sopépari	r	t	p	BYE
Senecio hartwegii	sopépari	r	c,ap	in	PN
Senecio sp.	tcukuá	w	c,ap	s,bl	BZ
Stevia salicifolia		r,s,l	ap,m	ta	PN
Stevia salicifolia		<u>l</u>	<u>c,ap</u>	<u>s,at</u>	PN
Stevia serrata	ronínowa	r,s,l	ap,m	ta	PN
Stevia serrata		<u>l</u>	<u>c,ap</u>	<u>s,at</u>	PN
Stevia sp.	ronino, rituvawa, wayusari	r	p,w	wd	BYE
Stevia sp.		w	p	bt	BYE
Stevia sp.		l	t	c,f,gi	BYE
Stevia sp.		r	t	p	BYE
Stevia sp.	hierba de la mula[+]	l	t	cl	BZ
Tagetes lucida	basigó	l	t	gi,m,hd, co,ch	BYE
Tagetes lucida	bashigo, bashigóko	l	t	gi,m	PN
Tagetes lucida	la coronilla[+]	l	t,a	pn	BZ
Tagetes lucida		l	t	m	PM
Tagetes micrantha	yeyésowa	w	t	gi,m	BYE
Tagetes micrantha		l	t	f,gi	PM
Taraxacum sp.	kolorba	l,r	t	co	BYE
Tithonia fruticosa	sewáchari	fl	c,t	co	PN

Botanical Name	Native Name	Plant Part	Form of Admin.	Ailment Treated	Source
Viguiera decurrens	nakaori	r	t	gi	BYE
Viguiera decurrens	nakáruri	r	c,p	bl,wd	PN
Zexmenia podocephala	reyóchari	r	t,r	gi	BYE
Zexmenia podocephala	keyóchuri, geóchuri	r	t	gi	PN
Zexmenia podocephala		r		m	PM
CONVOLVULACEAE					
Dichondra repens	bajuísuri	l	w	sw	PN
CRASSULACEAE					
Echeveria chihuahuaensis & *E. craigiana*	matagoche	l,j	ap	ey	BYE
Echeveria chihuahuaensis & *E. craigiana*		l	p,ap	ta	BYE
CUCURBITACEAE					
Cucurbita foetidissima	arisiki	r	t	gi,hd,p	BYE
Cucurbita foetidissima		r	w	f,h	BYE
Cucurbita foetidissima		r	t	p	PM
ERICACEAE					
Arctostaphylos pungens	wíchari	l	w	s	BYE
Arctostaphylos pungens	uwí	l	t	cc,lg	PN
Chimaphila maculata	rojásoa	l	ts	cu,m	BYE
EUPHORBIACEAE					
Acalypha sp.	pasmo[+]	l	t	m	BYE
Acalypha sp.		l	w	wd	BYE
Croton fragilis	chikókawi	b,s,rs	ap,m	ta	BYE
Croton fragilis		b,l,s	t	co,th	BYE
Croton niveus		b	c,bo,t	u	PN
Croton niveus	sikókowi	b	c,bo,t	ba	BZ
Croton sp.	sanilí	b	t	pai	BZ
Euphorbia heterophylla		r	r,bo	f	BZ
Euphorbia plicata	kusí sigóname	lt	ap	s,wd	BYE
Euphorbia sp.	yerba de la golondrina[+]	l	c,i,w	b,s if,wd	PN
Jatropha cordata	mata muchochos[+]	l	c,p	s	PM
Jatropha cordata		l	w	m	PM
Jatropha curcas		j	ap	ey	PN
Jatropha curcas		j	ap	ta,ey	BZ
Jatropha malacophylla	ratowa, sangregrado[+]	w,l	ap	ta,m	BYE
Ricinus communis	oliarka	sd		m	BYE
Ricinus communis		sd,l	p	if,b,sw, bl	PN
Ricinus communis		sd	r	gi	PN
Ricinus communis	oliráki	l	p	hd	BZ
Ricinus communis		l	o	s	BZ
Sapium biloculare	yerba de la flecha[+]	b,lt	i	p	PN
Sapium biloculare		lt		p	PM

Botanical Name	Native Name	Plant Part	Form of Admin.	Ailment Treated	Source
Sebastiana pavoniana	chuchí	lt	i	p	BYE
*Sebastiana pavoniana**		lt	i	p	PN
Tragia nepetifolia	ra'uli, ra'oke	l	t	f	BYE
Tragia nepetifolia		l	ap	hd	BYE
Tragia ramosa	ránuriki	l	w	s	BYE
Tragia ramosa	ŕauríki	l	t	he	PN
FAGACEAE					
Quercus arizonica		b	c,o	if,pa	PN
Quercus chihuahuensis	rojá	j	t	he,pr	PN
Quercus viminea		l	t	gi	PN
FOUQUIERACEAE					
Fouquieria macdougalii	simuchí	b,s	ap,t	ta	BYE
Fouquieria macdougalii		b	w	h,wc	BYE
(Fouquieria fasciculata)	simutcí tcuwalá	b	c	h,wc	BZ
FUMARIACEAE					
Corydalis aurea var. *occidentalis*	cylandrilla[+]	w	t	cb	H
GENTIANACEAE					
Gentiana sp.	matesa	w	t	cc	BYE
Gentiana sp.		w	w	h,wc	BYE
Stemmadenia palmeri		lt	p	ey	PN
Stemmadenia palmeri		lt	c,ap	bl,s	PN
GERANIACEAE					
Erodium cicutarium	semuchi	w	i	co,th,gi	PN
Erodium cicutarium		l	c,ap	er	PN
Geranium niveum	makiki	r	t	p	BYE
Geranium sp.	yerba de grippe[+]	r,l	t	co	BYE
KRAMERIACEAE					
Krameria sp.	wetahúpatci	b	c,o	ta	BZ
LABIATAE					
Agastache pallida		l	ap	ns	BZ
Agastache pallida			t	c,co	BZ⁻
Brittonastrum aurantiacum	umichi	l	t	cc,f,gi	BYE
Brittonastrum barberi	húpachi	l	t	he,st,dr	BYE
Brittonastrum barberi		w	t	f,gi	PM
Brittonasturm micranthum	húpachi	w	t	c,co,gi, dr,sl	BYE
Brittonastrum pringlei	húpachi	w	t	gi,sl	BYE
Brittonastrum pringlei		w	t	f,gi	PM
Hedeoma dentatum	chopénara	r,l	c,vp	c	PN
Hyptis albida		l	t	cb	PN
Hyptis albida		fl	ap	er	PN
Hyptis albida		w	c,ap	r	PN
Hyptis albida		l	t	r	PM
Hyptis albida		l	ap	er	PM
Hyptis emoryi	dosábali	w	t	cb	BZ
Hyptis spp.	rosáwori	l	t	he,wt, hd,f	BYE

Botanical Name	Native Name	Plant Part	Form of Admin.	Ailment Treated	Source
Marrubium vulgare	rouwaka	l	t	c	BYE
Mentha canadensis	yerba buena[+]	l	t	c,gi	BYE
Mentha canadensis			t	gi	PN
*Mentha canadensis**	bawéna	l	ap,t	ta	BZ
Monarda austromontana	napa	w	t	th,gi, co,m	BYE
Monarda austromontana		w	mix,a	f	BYE
Prunella vulgaris	napá	l	t	m	BYE
Salvia melissodora	salvia[+]	l	t	f	PM
Salvia tiliaefolia	chulisi	w	t	gi,hd	BYE

LAURACEAE

Botanical Name	Native Name	Plant Part	Form of Admin.	Ailment Treated	Source
Litsea glaucescens var. subsolitaria	laurél[+]	l	t	gi,m	BYE
Litsea glaucescens		l	t	gi	PN
Litsea glaucescens		l	t	cl	BZ
Litsea glaucescens		l	t	m	H

LEGUMINOSAE

Botanical Name	Native Name	Plant Part	Form of Admin.	Ailment Treated	Source
Acacia cymbispina	wichaka	sp	t	k	PN
Acacia farnesiana	wichaka	fl	w	ey	BYE
Acacia farnesiana	wichaka	sp	t	k	PN
Acacia farnesiana		fl	c,o,p	hd,b	PN
Acacia farnesiana	mokowí	b,sp	t	bt	BZ
(Caesalpinia mexicana)	babálatci	r	c	wd,s,ul	BZ
Caesalpinia platyloba	palo colorado[+]	l	w	ta	BYE
Caesalpinia platyloba		b	ap	ta	BYE
Caesalpinia pulcherrima	makapal	r	w	f	BYE
Caesalpinia pulcherrima	tavachín	r	t	ve	PN
Calliandra eriophylla	brasilillo[+]	w	t	ve	PN
Calliandra humilis var. reticulata	riwérame	sd	r	sl	PN
Cologania angustifolia	perrito[+]	r	t	p	H
Cologania sp.	bisiki	w	t	m	BYE
Coursetia glandulosa	samo, arí	/e/	t	gi,m	BYE
Coursetia glandulosa		/e/	mix	hd	BYE
*Coursetia glandulosa**	samo[+]	/e/	c,i	f,dy	PN
Coursetia glandulosa		/e/	r	gi	H
Coursetia glandulosa		/e/	t	k	I
Dalea polygonoides		l	c,t	hd	PN
Dalea wislizenii	hierba de piojo[+]	w	w	in	H
Dalea sp.	selogoni, ronóraso	l	t	gi,dr	BYE
Erythrina flabelliformis	kaposí	sd	p,w	s,ey,wd	BYE
Erythrina flabelliformis		sd	t	hd	BYE
Erythrina flabelliformis	aposhí, aposhiki	sd	c,i	vm	PN
Erythrina flabelliformis		sd	c	ta	PN
Erythrina flabelliformis		sd	i	gi	PN
*Erythrina flabelliformis**	aposí	sd	c,i	gi	BZ
Erythrina flabelliformis		sd		vm	PM
Eysenhardtia polystachya		b	c,t	pai	PN
Haematoxylon brasiletto	sitagape	b,wd	t	dr	BYE
Haematoxylon brasiletto		wd	c,w	j	PN
Haematoxylon brasiletto	sitákame	wd	bo,w	j	BZ
Lysiloma divaricata	wapakuwe	b	ap	ta	BYE
Lysiloma divaricata		b	t	gi	BYE

Botanical Name	Native Name	Plant Part	Form of Admin.	Ailment Treated	Source
Lysiloma watsonii	mechowí	b	ap	ta	BYE
Lysiloma watsonii		b	t	m	BYE
Lysiloma watsonii	mechawíki	b	t	ve	PN
Melilotus indica	trébol	l	c,p	hd	PN
Phaseolus metcalfei	gotóko, otóko, gotó	r	t	gi	PN
Pithecellobium dulce	wamútcali	l	bo,w	ey	BZ
Prosopis glandulosa	mesquite[+]	b,l	w	ey	BYE
Prosopis glandulosa		l	p	ey	BYE
Psoralea trinervata	contra yerba[+]	r,w	t	f	PM
Rhynchosia pyramidalis	munísowa	sd	c,o,p	r,bk	PN
Tephrosia leiocarpa	nawé, nawéke	r	c,p	in	PN
Willardia mexicana	haví	b	w	in,h	BYE
Willardia mexicana		b		in	PM
Zornia reticulata	yerba de la víbora[+]	w	t	f,if,hd	BYE
*Zornia reticulata**	yerba de la víbora[+]		t	f	PN
Zornia reticulata		w	t	ch	I
Zornia venosa	yerba de la víbora[+]	w	t	f	BYE

LENTIBULARIACEAE

Botanical Name	Native Name	Plant Part	Form of Admin.	Ailment Treated	Source
Utricularia sp.	koliso	w	p	s	BYE

LINACEAE

Botanical Name	Native Name	Plant Part	Form of Admin.	Ailment Treated	Source
Linum sp.	rukévari	r	t	co	BYE

LOGANIACEAE

Botanical Name	Native Name	Plant Part	Form of Admin.	Ailment Treated	Source
Buddleia cordata	matowi	l		m	BYE
Buddleia cordata		l	p	bl,s	PN
Buddleia cordata	batówi	l	p,o	wd,b	BZ
Buddleia sessiliflora	mató	l	p	bl,s	PN
Buddleia sp.	wasálawa	wd	bo,w	fr,cu	BZ

LORANTHACEAE

Botanical Name	Native Name	Plant Part	Form of Admin.	Ailment Treated	Source
Phoradendron sp.	kuchóoko	w	t	co,gi, ve,p	BYE

MALPIGHIACEAE

Botanical Name	Native Name	Plant Part	Form of Admin.	Ailment Treated	Source
Mascagnia macroptera	matenene	w	t	ml	BYE
Mascagnia macroptera		b	c,p	bb,sp	PN
Mascagnia macroptera	anaraka	b	c,o,p	ta	PN
Thryallis glauca		l	t	dr	PN
Thryallis glauca		l	w	wd	PN

MALVACEAE

Botanical Name	Native Name	Plant Part	Form of Admin.	Ailment Treated	Source
Abutilon trisulcatum	malva[+]	j	w	h	BZ
Anoda triangularis	tutsji	l	r	f	L
Malva parviflora	malva[+]	w	t,w	cb,hd,gi f,m,k	BYE
Malva parviflora		w	p	s	BYE
Malva parviflora		l	o	s	PN
Malva parviflora		l	t	p	PN
Malva parviflora		w	i,en	p	PN
Sida rhombifolia	malva+	j	w	h	BZ

Botanical Name	Native Name	Plant Part	Form of Admin.	Ailment Treated	Source
MARTYNIACEAE					
Martynia annua	surechi	fr	t	hd	BYE
MORACEAE					
Dorstenia drakeana	o'chala	r	t	he	BYE
Ficus petiolaris	watorí	lt	ap	wd,bb	BYE
Ficus petiolaris		l	i	fr	BYE
Ficus petiolaris	watorí, tescalama[+]	lt	w	wd	PN
Ficus petiolaris	tcitóliki	lt	p	pa	BZ
Morus microphylla	apurí	b	i	p	BYE
MYRTACEAE					
Psidium sartorianum	rowilí	fr,l	p	s,wd	BYE
NYCTAGINACEAE					
Boerhaavia viscosa	saramba	w,r	t	ms	BYE
Mirabilis jalapa	maravilla[+]	fl	t	he	BYE
Pisonia capitata	agoko	b	t	f	BYE
Pisonia capitata	galóko, galó tcókame	l	c,i	f	BZ
PASSIFLORACEAE					
Passiflora foetida var. *gossypifolia*	bolita[+]	w	t	dr,f	BYE
PHYTOLACCACEAE					
Phytolacca sp.	lário	r	t	pb	BYE
Phytolacca sp.		fl	p	bt	BYE
PIPERACEAE					
Piper sp.	kurúvia	s	cn	r	BYE
Piper sp.		l	in	cu	BYE
Piper sp.	kokolmíka	s	cn	pa	BZ
Piper sp.			w	r	BZ
PLANTAGINACEAE					
(*Plantago major*)	foró, lantén		t	cn	PN
Plantago sp.	yerba del pastor[+]	sd,w	t	gi	BYE
PLATANACEAE					
Platanus wrightii	sa'á	b	t	m	BYE
Platanus wrightii	ushako, fepogá	b	c,t	m	PN
PLUMBAGINACEAE					
Plumbago scandens	rochinúe	r	w,p	wd	BYE
Plumbago scandens		r,wd	c,t	gi,r	PN
POLYGONACEAE					
Eriogonum atrorubens	bariguchi	r	r,m	co	BYE
Eriogonum atrorubens	bariguchi	r	bo,e	lg	PN
Eriogonum atrorubens		r	m	ta,ag	PM
Eriogonum atrorubens		r	m	ag	H
Eriogonum undulatum	bariguchi	r	bo,e	lg	PN

Botanical Name	Native Name	Plant Part	Form of Admin.	Ailment Treated	Source
Rumex crispus	eviloriva	r	t	dr	BYE
Rumex crispus		l	p	s	BYE
PUNICACEAE					
Punica granatum	granada+	fr	p	bl,an	BYE
Punica granatum		fr	mix	bu,cc	I
RANUNCULACEAE					
Aquilegia skinneri	perico+	r	p	b	H
Ranunculus aquatilis	koliso	w	p	s,wd	BYE
Ranunculus hydrocharoides	mosaroko	l	t	m	BYE
Thalictrum fendleri var. wrightii	kachano	w	w	m	BYE
*Thalictrum fendleri wrightii**		l	t,w	ht	PN
Thalictrum pinnatrum	visiki	r	t	co	BYE
RHAMNACEAE					
Ceanothus buxifolius	wicháoko	r	t	m,dr	BYE
Gouania lupuloides	waniwaka	fr,l	w	at	BYE
Karwinskia humboldtiana	kusí júkame	b	c,t	f	PN
Karwinskia humboldtiana	amulí	l	p	hd	BZ
ROSACEAE					
Cercocarpus montanus	chikáka	l	t	c,cn,dy	PN
Cercocarpus montanus		r	c,p	s	PN
Potentilla thurberi	yerba colorado+	r	t	co,dr, th,gi	BYE
Potentilla thurberi		r	ap	ta	BYE
Prunus brachybotrya	ko	l	e	in	BZ
(Prunus capuli)	usábi	l	t	co,cc	PN
Purshia tridentata	chagúnari	l	c,p	bl	PN
RUBIACEAE					
Bouvardia glaberrima	rurikuchi	s,l	t	he	PN
Hintonia latiflora	iwíchuri, iwígiri	b	t	pb,f,m	BYE
Hintonia latiflora		b,l	w,c	s	BYE
*Hintonia latiflora**	copalquín+	b	t	f,gi	PN
*Hintonia latiflora**	iwítculi	b	t	f	BZ
*Hintonia latiflora**		l	c	s	BZ
Hintonia latiflora		b	t,b	f,ml	PM
Hintonia latiflora		b	c	s,ul	PM
Hintonia latiflora		b	a	n	H
RUTACEAE					
Citrus spp.		l,fr	r,t	hd,c	BYE
Ptelea trifoliata	opoa	b	t	m	BYE
Ptelea trifoliata		l	p	hd	BYE
Ptelea trifoliata	upaga	l,r	w	r	PN
Ptelea trifoliata	ápago	l	bo,w	r	BZ
Ruta chalapensis	ruda+	l,s	t	gi	BYE
Ruta chalapensis		l	w	er	BYE
Ruta chalapensis		l,r	i	gi	PN
Ruta chalapensis		l	c,ap	er	PN

Botanical Name	Native Name	Plant Part	Form of Admin.	Ailment Treated	Source
SALICACEAE					
Populus angustifolia	usaroko	b	t	k	BYE
Populus tremuloides	usaroko	b	t	m	BYE
Populus tremuloides	wisaró	b	t	cb	PN
SAPINDACEAE					
Cardiospermum halicacabum	rayó[+]	fr,s	t	gi	PN
Serjania mexicana	diente de culebra[+]	l,s	w	r	BYE
Serjania mexicana	sinówi ramirá	s	p	b,sp,bb	PN
Serjania mexicana	diente de víbora[+]	s	ap	r,pa	BZ
Serjania mexicana		fl,s	c,t	pr	PN
SAXIFRAGACEAE					
Ribes neglectum		l	p	hd	PN
SCROPHULARIACEAE					
Castilleja spp.	flor de piedras[+]	fl,l	t	k,he,bp, gi	BYE
Penstemon campanulatus	hablorias[+]	l	t	ab	BYE
Penstemon campanulatus		l	p,w	s,b,if	BYE
Penstemon barbatus	boteya[+]	r,w	t	he	BYE
Penstemon barbatus		r	ap	ta	BYE
Penstemon barbatus		w	w	s	BYE
Russelia sarmentosa	pinito[+]	w	t	f	H
SOLANACEAE					
Capsicum annuum var. glabriusculum	korí sivre	fr	mix	m,hd	BYE
Capsicum annuum var. glabriusculum		fr		m	BYE
Datura discolor	uchiri	l		m	BYE
Datura inoxia	uchiri	l		m	BYE
*Datura inoxia**	tikúwarí	l	p	sp,if	PN
*Datura inoxia**	dekúba	l	p	hd	BZ
Datura inoxia		l	w	ul	PM
Datura inoxia		l	sm	as	PM
Nicotiana glauca		l	p	hd	BZ
Nicotiana glauca	wipáka	l	p	hd	PN
Nicotiana rustica	wipá	l	p	bt	BYE
Nicotiana rustica		l	sm	cu	BYE
Nicotiana tabacum	makuchi	l	sm	cu	BYE
Nicotiana sp.			m,ap	bt	BZ
Physalis sp.	tomatillo[+]	fr	i,p	th	BYE
Solanum americanum-nigrum complex	chichikalite	l,fr	p,w	wd,s	BYE
*Solanum americanum-nigrum complex**		l	bo,p	r	PN
*Solanum americanum-nigrum complex**	tcítcikalíte	s,l	bo,p	pn	BZ
Solanum diversifolium	wiígame	w	w	r	PN
Solanum diversifolium		w	t	c	PN
Solanum rostratum	soíwari	l	t	mn	PN
Solanum verbascifolium	hikuli	l	p	hd,p,wd	BYE
Solanum verbascifolium		l	p	s	PN

Botanical Name	Native Name	Plant Part	Form of Admin.	Ailment Treated	Source
Solanum verbascifolium		l	p	s,wd	BZ
TILIACEAE					
Heliocarpus attenuatus	saníwari	b	t	v,mn,cb	BYE
Heliocarpus palmeri	saníwari	b	w	h,bb	BYE
TURNERACEAE					
Turnera ulmifolia	saráame	l	t	dr	PN
UMBELLIFERAE					
Conioselinum mexicanum	matarí	r	p,t	r	BYE
Conioselinum mexicanum		r	t	pn,co,gi	H
Conium maculatum		r		m	BYE
Daucus montanus	chipúnue	l	p	s,wd	BYE
Daucus montanus		l	ap	er	BYE
Eryngium carlinae	saibari	w	t	m,gi,cc	BYE
Eryngium carlinae	soíwari	fl	c,p	ey	PN
Eryngium heterophyllum	sawíwari	w,r	t	dr,cc, ey,he	BYE
Eryngium heterophyllum		fl,l	t	co	PN
*Eryngium heterophyllum**	hutátci		bo,t	co,hd	BZ
Eryngium longifolium	chinaka	w	t	cc	BYE
Ligusticum porteri	wa'sia	r	t,a,w	gi,hd,f	BYE
Ligusticum porteri	washía	r	c,bo,w	r	PN
Ligusticum porteri		r,l	c,t	gi	PN
Ligusticum porteri		r	t	pn,co,gi	H
Prionosciadium thapsoides var. *pringlei*	kusari	r		m	BYE
Prionosciadium thapsoides var. *pringlei**	kusalí	r	c,t	cc,f	BZ
Prionosciadium townsendi	saraviki	r		m	BYE
Prionosciadium townsendi		r	t	f	I
Prionosciadium townsendi		r	r	hp	I
Tauschia tarahumara	húve	r	ap	ta	BYE
URTICACEAE					
Urera caracasana	rá'yo	l,fr	t	pa	BYE
Urtica dioica	ra'nurí	l	t	hd,ms	BYE
VALERIANACEAE					
Valeriana edulis	chinonua	r	t	m	BYE
VERBENACEAE					
Lantana sp.	peonia[+]	r	c,o	cu,lg	BZ
Lantana sp.		r	c,t	gi,cb	BZ
Verbena carolinae	wahíchuri	l	ap	ta	BYE
Verbena carolinae		l	t	gi	BYE
Verbena carolinae		l	t	wd,s	BYE
*Verbena carolinae**	verbena[+]	l	p	bl,b	PN
*Verbena carolinae**		fl	t	b	PN
*Verbena carolinae**		r	c,p	bl	PN
*Verbena carolinae**		fl	w	wd	PN
Verbena elegans var. *asperata*	anariye	l	p	s,wd	BYE

Botanical Name	Native Name	Plant Part	Form of Admin.	Ailment Treated	Source
Verbena elegans var. asperata		l	t	he	BYE
Verbena wrightii	moradilla[+]	w	t	f	BZ
Vitex mollis	jalí	j	ap	bt	BYE
Vitex mollis		l	t	fr	BYE
Vitex mollis	jarí	l	t	f	PN
Vitex mollis	halíki	s,l	t	f	BZ
VITACEAE					
Cissus sp.	walé	j,s	cs	bb	BZ
Vitis arizonica	urí	r	t	cb	BYE

Table 3

Concordance of Plant Names

Botanical Name from Literature	Source	Botanical Name as Shown in Table 2
Aristolochia brevipes	BZ:176; PN:180	*Aristolochia wrightii*
Cacalia decomposita	BZ:175; PN:191	*Psacalium decompositum*
Cheilanthes kaulfussii	PN:178	*Cheilanthes pyramidalis*
Coutarea latiflora	PN:190	*Hintonia latiflora*
Coutarea pterosperma	BZ:169; PN:191	*Hintonia latiflora*
Datura meteloides	BZ:138; PN:189	*Datura inoxia*
Eryngium sp.	BZ:144	*Eryngium heterophyllum*
Erythrina sp.	BZ:170	*Erythrina flabelliformis*
Juniperus pachyphlaea	PN:171, 178	*Juniperus deppeana*
Mentha sp.	BZ:144	*Mentha canadensis*
Phragmites communis	PN:179	*Phragmites australis*
Sebastiana pringlei	PN:185	*Sebastiana pavoniana*
Solanum nigrum	BZ:168; PN:189	*Solanum americanum-nigrum complex*
Tabebuia palmeri	PN:190	*Tabebuia chrysantha*
Thalictrum fendleri	PN:181	*Thalictrum fendleri* var. *wrightii*
Umbelliferae (unidentified genus)	BZ:144	*Prionosciadium thapsoides* var. *pringlei*
Verbena caroliniana	PN:188	*Verbena carolinae*
Willardia mexicana	PN:183	*Coursetia glandulosa*
Yucca decipiens	BZ:164	*Yucca schottii*
Zornia diphylla	PN:183	*Zornia reticulata*

BZ = Bennett and Zingg (1935)
PN = Pennington (1963)

TARAHUMARA SHAMANISM

Spencer L. Rogers

Until the year 1620, the Tarahumara occupied nearly the entire state of Chihuahua. After that time, Spanish colonization forced the Indians to withdraw into the more remote, mountainous regions of the Sierra Madre range, where they now reside. The total number of Tarahumara is difficult to determine since it is impossible to conduct a reliable census survey of that population. The census of 1950 enumerated 18,421 individuals over five years of age, but some estimates have been as high as 30,000. It is certain that they form the most numerous aboriginal group in Mexico north of the Federal District.

As a result of the mountainous and inhospitable terrain in which they have lived, the Tarahumara did not establish themselves in villages as did the Hopi of Arizona but tended to live each family unto itself in cave habitations or simple log or stone structures. The obstacles to mobility and communication did not prevent their traveling (Di Peso 1966:9) and acquiring social concepts and supernatural doctrines from other North American peoples. Yet their mythologic beliefs are colored to a considerable degree by their isolated existence in a region where their most stimulating reflective experience was perhaps related to their view of the night sky made dramatic by a confining framework of towering and rugged mountain peaks.

The ritual life and supernatural healing ministrations centered around the social and iatric role of the shaman. The Tarahumara shaman, called *oueruame* in their language, is a priest, healer, and specialist in the supernatural. The most renowned shamans have been trained for the profession in one village, Nararachic ("the place of weeping"), which seems to have served as a seminary. A number of older shamans have dwelt there who have more or less systematically passed their lore on to younger aspirants in the profession. The shaman has three essential functions: healing the sick; supervising ritual events; and providing, conserving, and managing the use of peyote, which is regarded as a supernatural substance. Before discussing their shamanistic techniques, it is important to review two subjects: the Tarahumara's ancient traditional concept of the universe and the influence exerted by Christianity on the symbolism of Tarahumara rites.

Tarahumara ideas about the origin of the earth, the gods, and man are somewhat varied, but a few ideas seem widely held. It was commonly believed that the union of the sun and moon brought forth mankind. Another idea was that a previous world existed either in space or in some mythical region connected with the present world. It was generally thought that the Tarahumara occupied the center of the world and were the first people (Basauri 1929:50), and also that the white races were not the descendants of the sun but had an unknown origin. Fire was of divine origin, since the rays of the sun, their prime divinity, can produce it. The first men sprang spontaneously from the soil and had a short life, but their descendants became more robust and lived longer, gradually attaining the longevity of present-day people.

There are no traces of totemism or reverence for particular animals in Tarahumara culture (Basauri 1929:50). They freely kill any wild animal and often sacrifice domestic animals during festivals, utilizing, on these occasions, the meat for food. They kill lambs, goats, and cattle for sacrifice through bleeding. The blood is collected in a wooden cup and thrown in the direction of the four cardinal points. In the place where a sacrifice is held, a wooden cross is erected and kept in place during the entire time that the rite is in progress. The only ceremonies that concern plants are those in regard to peyote, which is considered divine in orgin, and the green corn ceremony which commemorates the ripening of maize--the source of both food and spirituous drink.

With the introduction of Christianity into the world of the Tarahumara, certain symbolisms and rites came into use in varying degrees of involvement. In general, Roman Catholic doctrine has been rather slight in its effect on the deeper thoughts, feelings, and actions of the Tarahumara, but even so, they adopted a number of symbols with considerable enthusiasm. The use of the cross and crucifix, the manual sign of the cross, and the rosary are in common use, often in combination with aboriginal observances. The Christian meaning of these symbols is often lost or highly modified. The basic religious philosophy of the Tarahumara was apparently dualistic, with a father and a mother divinity. This appears to have passed over into Christian theology through the concept of God the Father and the Virgin Mary, which are associated with the aboriginal belief in the Father Sun and Mother Moon (Lumholtz 1902 (I):295). The concept of the Trinity seems to have somewhat permeated their thinking, and three major crosses are commonly set up during fiestas. The morning star seems to have been revered to form a supernatural trilogy.

Crosses used by the Tarahumara, while appearing to be the Latin cross of Christian tradition introduced by the Jesuit fathers, are often carved in such a manner that the upper portion forms an equal-armed cross with the lower arm being merely an extension for support. The equal-armed cross in New World symbology commonly represents the four directions and cardinal points, and it is quite likely that among the Tarahumara the cross used in fiestas and sacrificial rites is a slightly Christianized version of an aboriginal orientation symbol. It also becomes the symbol of the Sun Father and the peyote cult (Alexander 1936: 176-177).

The Trinity concept, however, is at least superficially established in the formula "God is one with three distinct persons," which has been commonly memorized. Their beliefs involve a concept of Heaven and of Hell. There are three levels of Heaven. A person in his afterlife progresses through one, dies, and goes to the next; likewise, there are three Hells, where people go who have violated the basic ethical principles of life. The journey through the underworld involves passing through huge fires which consume the unworthy. All this is rather vague and Satan does not appear as a dynamic personality. On the other hand, Judas is quite specific and appears in sculptured form during Easter fiestas and is often burned in effigy.

Soul theory among the Tarahumara is rather complex. The soul is located in the heart. Air passes through the heart; the lungs give strength to the heart. The soul leaves the heart when a person dies. The soul is the seat of feelings. If a person is tired, he must breathe hard so that his soul will not escape. The soul wanders in dreams and may be captured by the Water People, in which case a shaman must be engaged to bring it back. If a child comes in contact with a rattlesnake and becomes frightened, the snake eats the soul of the child and makes him sick. When a healing shaman is summoned, he will breathe upon the body. His breath gives strength and aid to the frightened soul of the stricken person. The shaman takes *tesgüino*, a native beer, to strengthen his own soul and prevent illness to himself.

One can learn many things from dreams. Shamans especially must give attention to the import of dreams. Dreams may predict the oncoming of drought or disease. Souls of the dead may inform the shaman when to institute dances that will avoid disasters.

There are several grades of shamans and healers among the Tarahumara, all differing in their roles and the degree of prestige which they enjoy. The highest rank of shaman has a reputation for numerous successful healings and competence in dealing with the supernatural through forecasting and averting various misadventures that affect the community. Such shamans receive the homage and respect of the people and, at times, are feared. There are lesser grades of practitioners, some of whom act as assistants to the senior grade professionals and serve only part time, living usually as do other people of the community. Another level of healer is the herbalist, whose main skill is in a knowledge of the healing properties of herbs. They use the plants of the region but now may also use Western medicines. In addition, there are chanters or singers who do no healing but are participants in the various rites through their knowledge of the songs and ritual procedures.

Tarahumara culture differs from many other aboriginal societies in that a person cannot become a shaman through dreams or supernatural revelation alone; he must pass through a period of training under a senior practitioner. The shamanistic calling often is transmitted through family lines--from father to son or from brother to brother. The instructor shamans usually teach their protégés without pay, but some may sell their knowledge. Training consists of learning the songs, the arts and skills of curing and other rites, and the psychological niceties of the profession. Study may take as long as three years. There is no formal ceremony of graduation at the end of a training period. When an aspiring shaman is considered competent by his instructor, the older man will permit his student to officiate at a healing rite and then approve of his performance, thereby signaling the younger man's entrance into the profession. The shamanistic profession requires a considerable degree of restraint and self-control on the part of its members. The shaman must give the impression of self-assured competence and dignity, which requires him to be somewhat aloof from ordinary citizens. He must remain sober, more or less, although this is difficult since by custom it

is neccessary for him to imbibe freely of *tesgüino*, a beer made of corn
and various other plants (see Bye, Medicinal Plants of the Tarahumara,
Table 1, this volume) fermented to an alcohol content of around 10 per-
cent. This is a traditional and highly regarded adjunct at all fiestas,
work parties, and any public gatherings, serious or convivial (Bennett
and Zingg 1935:257). Shamans are normally paid quite well for their
services, usually in the form of food or domestic animals. A shaman is
not held culpable for failures to heal a sick patient, although successful cures advance his reputation and unsuccessful ministrations detract
from it with the resulting negative effect on community respect and
level of compensation.

A common cause of disease among the Tarahumara is the invasion of
the sufferer's body by a malignant spirit or an organism, maggots or
pieces of buckskin believed to be maggots, or bits of wood or stone
(Lumholtz 1902(I):317; Fried 1969:864). The healing technique accordingly is based upon the expulsion of the disease-causing entity from the
patient's body. A rite of exorcism may be used to evict a disease-
causing spirit, or the disease-causing organism may be sucked from the
patient's body through a reed tube, usually about five inches long
(Bennett and Zingg 1935:260). What the doctor removes by sucking from
the patient's body is spit into a bowl, carried around a fire three
times, and dumped into the ashes. Another cause of disease is soul
loss. If a part of the soul wanders away from the body, the patient becomes sick with chills and fever. The shaman, who may be called in to
treat the case, sends his soul out to retrieve the missing soul, which
action may require a payment of ransom to malicious beings who have captured the soul.

Although the healing rites are completely pagan in doctrine, a number of Christian symbols are important adjuncts to their execution. The
doctor wears a rosary--with crucifix attached. With this he will make
the sign of the cross over the patient's body and may put the crucifix
in his mouth and blow over it toward the patient. Crosses are erected
where shamanistic rites are to be performed.

Peyote is regarded as a powerful plant by the Tarahumara. "Peyote"
is a generic term for a number of species of cactus of the genus *Lophophora*. Its use is not widespread among the people, and it is employed
mainly in curing rites, often after other efforts have failed. Although
they use many medicinal plants--as many as 294 have been counted by
Fontana (1979:61; see also Bye, Medicinal Plants of the Tarahumara,
Table 2, this volume)--only certain shamans can acquire and use peyote.
Any misuse of it involves great danger. The eating of peyote is done
not for pleasure, but for healing purposes (Basauri 1929:36). The doctor, the patient, and some of the attendant group eat the plant, which
causes hallucinations consisting of lines and points of luminous colors,
pupil dilation, and an increase in pulse rate. It does not, however,
cause euphoria or mental disturbance and, as used by the Tarahumara, is
probably not addictive.

While recent practices pertaining to healing among the Tarahumara
are based on techniques of exorcism and object removal through blowing
and sucking, there is some evidence that in the past they practiced tre-
phining of the skull (Lumholtz and Hrdlička 1897:390-396; Lumholtz 1902

(I):327-329). Opening the skull, by cutting through the bone, was extensively practiced in Peru and Bolivia in South America but was rarely performed in North America. What this operation might have accomplished in Tarahumara culture is difficult to reconstruct, just as it is in other areas where it was practiced. Presently, there are three beliefs as to why the operation was performed in primitive cultures: 1) as a therapeutic device to alleviate the effect of skull fractures, 2) as a supplementary technique of shamanistic exorcism to release a malignant spirit from the patient's body, and 3) as a magical procedure to obtain a skull segment thought to have mystic powers. It is not known if any of these explanations apply to the Tarahumara.

Tarahumara shamans have functions other than healing the sick. These include bringing rain and avoiding disasters related to astronomical events. Their rain ceremony involves the building of a huge fire in the belief that the smoke will rise to the region above, become rain clouds, and cause the rain to fall. The rain ceremony may include the shaman drawing a line of fire with a smoldering pine stick while crossing himself in the four directions. Lumholtz (1902(I):32) describes one ceremony in which a sacrifice was held in order to cure the moon during its dark and debilitated phase.

Another role of the shaman involves his part in presiding at the fiesta after the birth of a child. He is not concerned with the process of birth. There are not even midwives. A woman about to give birth to a child is accompanied, if at all, by her husband or a woman friend who attends her, provides warm water, and cuts the umbilical cord of the newborn baby. The cord must be buried immediately in order to ensure the mental health of the child. After the birth (three days if a boy, four if a girl), a goat is killed, *tesgüino* provided, and a cross set up in the house. The shaman dedicates the *tesgüino* and serves part of it. The family kneels before him while he makes signs of the cross in the air with incense. He burns a bit of hair from each member of the family and blows a cross on the head of each person present. With this, the ritual is over, and the remaining part of the rite is a copious drinking of *tesgüino*. After the birth, the woman resumes her ordinary course of life except for a restriction on bathing for four days and not eating apples or calabashes for two or three weeks. The father, however, does not work for three days after his child is born, an aspect of the widespread *couvade* rite.

In conclusion, it may be noted that Tarahumara shamanism has much in common with shamanistic beliefs and practices of other North American aborigines, except for a few points. The extensive jumble of Christian symbolism with strictly pagan ministrations, while not unique, is noteworthy. The invariable drinking of *tesgüino* is significant, since many peoples who have made basic use of maize in their diets have never discovered or taken to the art of fermenting it for beverage purposes. Moreover, the Tarahumara developed interesting mores in regard to its consumption, making its use not only respectable but obligatory and supernaturally sanctioned.

The more highly regarded shamans have been powerful figures in the social structure and undoubtedly have effected many cures through the impact of their suggestive therapy.

110

REFERENCES CITED

Alexander, Hartley Burr
    1936   North American Mythology. Cambridge: The University Press.

Basauri, Carlos
    1929   Monografía de los Tarahumaras. México, D.F.: Talleres
            Gráficos de la Nación.

Bennett, Wendell C., and Robert M. Zingg
    1935   The Tarahumara: An Indian Tribe of Northern Mexico.
            Chicago: University of Chicago Press. (New edition with
            color photographs by L. G. Verplancken, S.J., published by
            Rio Grande Press, Inc., Glorieta, New Mexico, 1976).

Di Peso, Charles C.
    1966   Archaeology and Ethnology of the Northern Sierra.
            In: G. F. Ekholm and G. R. Willey, eds., Archaeological
            Frontiers and External Connections, pp. 3-25. Handbook of
            Middle American Indians, Vol. 4. Austin: University of
            Texas Press.

Fontana, Bernard L.
    1979   Tarahumara: Where Night is the Day of the Moon. Flagstaff:
            Northland Press.

Fried, Jacob
    1969   The Tarahumara. In: E. Z. Vogt ed., Ethnology, Part 2, pp.
            846-870. Handbook of Middle American Indians, Vol. 8.
            Austin: University of Texas Press.

Lumholtz, Carl
    1902   Unknown Mexico: A Record of Five Years' Exploration among
            the Tribes of the Western Sierra Madre; in the Tierra
            Caliente of Tepic and Jalisco; and among the Tarascos of
            Michoacan. Vols. I and II. New York: Charles Scribner's
            Sons.

Lumholtz, Carl, and Aleš Hrdlička
    1897   Trephining in Mexico. American Anthropologist 10:389-396.

ETHNOECOLOGICAL NOTES
FOR SOUTHWESTERN CHIHUAHUA

Robert A. Bye, Jr.

Ethnoecology can be seen as the investigation of the ecological bases of interactions and relationships between people and their ambient environment. In this paper, I will present a general framework for looking at the assumed interactions between a people similar to Tarahumara Indians (prior to European contact) and their varied environment in southwestern Chihuahua, Mexico. Specifics of interactions and details of processes will not be discussed, but they could easily be generated from such a framework. The following presentation is based upon archaeological, historical, and contemporary data derived from documents, literature, and personal experiences in the region east and southeast of the area where the mummies were discovered (see Tyson, this volume).

The general region from which the mummies originated is near the municipality of Santa Ana, Chínipas, Chihuahua, and is located in the watershed of Arroyo Loreto and Arroyo Vinata. This area is part of the westward draining Río Mayo system which flows through highly dissected canyons. A steep environmental gradient is associated with this rugged topography. Within a 10 kilometer radius, the elevation ranges from 700 meters along the river to over 2,000 meters in the surrounding peaks. It is assumed that between the time of the individuals preserved as mummies and today there has been little significant change in the climate, soil, and vegetation. Also, it is assumed that the plants and animals responded to climatic factors and human activities in the same manner as they do today. The people who lived at that time most likely moved freely within the varied environment as do the present-day Tarahumara. A day's journey would allow easy access to all the major ecological zones. The summer was more tolerably spent in the mountains while the cold winters would be avoided by a move to the sunny, warm slopes of the canyons.

The climatic pattern parallels general physiographic units. In the mountains, the cool humid mesothermal wet climate (Cwb) (Schmidt 1975) has a rainy season beginning in June-July and ending in November. Occasionally, snows may fall as the dry season begins in December. The dry season usually peaks in May and ends with the summer rains. The warm humid mesothermal wet climate (Cfa) (Schmidt 1975) in the barrancas is warmer and has a similar wet and dry seasonal cycle.

The soil is derived from the weathering of a dominant Tertiary cap of volcanic rock with scattered Mesozoic sedimentary and metamorphic outcrops and from the deposition of organic materials produced by vegetation. In general, it can be classified as a Mollisol (Bye 1983).

The vegetation, a response to the climatic and topographic factors, can be divided into three zones in the region (Bye 1983). In the upper zone (ca 1,525 m and higher), the Pine-Oak Forest is predominant. In the upper canyons (ca 915-1,525 m), the Barrancan Oak Woodland is abundant. At the lower elevations (915 m and less) of the upper drainage canyons, the Short Tree Forest is common. The exact ranges of elevation of these zones vary depending upon the exposure of the slopes.

The western slope of the Sierra Madre Occidental is very important due to the richness of biological resources along this environmental gradient in a relatively short distance. Also, this region is near the old main trail connecting the upper Río Mayo drainage and the Río Chínipas of the Río Fuerte drainage (Gentry 1942). Access to the area and movement within the various ecological zones by humans suggest possibilities for subsistence patterns and resource exploitation.

This paper will present some of the important plants and animals[1] as they are used today and could have been used in the past, with respect to each vegetation zone. The general order of presentation will be organisms associated with subsistence and maintenance of health based upon wild, anthropogenic, and cultivated resources; materials for manufacture (fuel, fiber, construction, and dyes); and other useful plants. Categories, e.g., ceremonial plants and folk taxonomies, will not be given.

The actual processes and relationships will not be discussed although certain assumptions are made. For instance, the health status of the people with respect to edible and medicinal plants is assumed to have been adequate yet variable. There are no reliable health studies among the present-day Tarahumara. Reports of diseases and malnutrition usually originate from Mexican populations or from Tarahumara populations near Mexican settlements and may reflect the effects of acculturation, as has been seen in other aspects of their life (Llaguno 1971). An early and crude analysis of a Tarahumara diet (Basauri 1929) suggests that the diet is adequate although not good. Agricultural practice was probably more limited in the past before Spanish contact and the introduction of plows and draft animals. Exploitation of trees for fuel and construction may have differed in intensity and technique before the availability of the metal axe.

PINE-OAK FOREST

The Pine-Oak Forest is dominated by various species of pines (*Pinus* spp.[2]) and oaks (*Quercus* spp.[3]). Juniper (*Juniperus* spp.) and madrone (*Arbutus* spp.) trees are locally common in some parts. Alder (*Alnus* spp.) and cypress (*Cupressus lindleyi*) are common along the drainages and follow the arroyos cutting down through the vertical vegetation belts into the Short Tree Forest.

Doves, pigeons, turkey, deer, racoons, opposums, skunks, squirrels, and snakes were hunted and trapped in the forest. From the end of the wet season and into the dry season, small fish--poisoned with such plants as knotweed (*Persicaria* spp.), cherry (*Prunus* spp.), and "sopepare" (*Roldona hartwegii*)--were gathered, smoked, and dried. In the spring, tadpoles were scooped from the shallow pools along arroyos while the pupae of the "iwiki" moth (*Eucheira socialis*) were collected in their silken bags on the madrone and eaten raw or cooked. The end of the dry season was a time to gather wild foods such as onion bulbs (*Allium* spp.) and oak galls (on *Quercus crassifolia*). With the early rains, edible wild greens of various wild carrot relatives (*Tauschia* spp.), edible fungi (*Amanita caesarea*, *Lepiota* spp.), and the quickly maturing fruits of gooseberries (*Ribes madrense*) were gathered. With the summer flowers, children chewed and sucked the sweet blossoms of red wild buckwheat (*Eriogonum atrorubens*) and honeysuckles (*Lonicera* spp.). The fall signaled the time to collect wild grapes (*Vitis arizonica*) and tubers of wild potato (*Solanum fendleri*).

Agricultural fields were restricted to areas where the soil was easy to turn and could be enriched naturally or by the application of bat dung. The alluvial shelves of the arroyos left by the receding streams and the interface of the open llanos with the steep, eroding slopes would be suitable areas. Figure 1 shows agricultural fields south of Tarahumara country in the territory of the neighboring Tepehuan.

Staple cultivated plants included maize (*Zea mays*) with such races as *Cristalino de Chihuahua* (yellow flint), *Apachito* (red flint), *Blanco* (white flint), and *Azul* (blue flour); beans (*Phaseolus vulgaris*, *P. coccineus*); and squashes (*Cucurbita pepo*, *C. ficifolia*). Grain amaranth (*Amaranthus hypochondriacus*) and leafy peppergrass (*Lepidium* sp.) would

Figure 1. Maize fields, cultivated by plow method, in the valley of Nabogame, Tepehuan territory, southwestern Chihuahua, Mexico (photograph courtesy of Howard Scott Gentry).

have been planted in disturbed areas (e.g., rubbish piles) near the dwellings. Although not cultivated, a number of edible plants were found in association with cultivation practice and were important components in the subsistence pattern. Various quelites--leafy greens such as peppergrass (*Lepidium* spp.), goosefoot (*Chenopodium berlandieri*), pigweed (*Amaranthus retroflexus*), and purslane (*Portulaca oleracea*)--were common during the planting season of May and early June. In the mid to late summer, corn smut (*Ustilago zeae*) would have been gathered as a great delicacy. During the fall harvests, fruits of husk tomato (*Physalis* spp.), sand cherry (*Jaltomata procumbens*), and brome grass (*Bromus* spp.) were gathered from the fields and used in preparing fresh food as well as being stored for later consumption. Fauna attracted to the cultivated fields provided animal protein. Traps or slingshots were used to kill gophers, rabbits, and lizards, while gathering activities provided grasshoppers, locusts, and corn worms. This activity also provided a means of reducing competitors for the cultivated food.

A trip to the woods in the late summer or fall supplied medicinal herbs for storage and later use in treating gastrointestinal disorders, colds, headaches, and wounds; these plants included horse-mint (*Monarda austromontana*), hyssop (*Agastache* spp.), and sweet marigold (*Tagetes lucida*). "Matarique" (*Psacalium decompositum*) roots, "kachana" (*Iostephane madrensis*), and lovage (*Ligusticum porteri*) were excavated and dried for future use in relieving muscle and joint aches. During the growing season, the cultivated fields provided such medicinal herbs as wormseed (*Chenopodium ambrosioides*) and prickly poppy (*Argemone mexicana*) as remedies for stomach disorders and wounds.

For construction associated with rock and cave shelters, the trunks of pines, junipers, and cypress provided support and foundation material, while the branches of willow (*Salix* spp.) and grass shoots of *Muhlenbergia* spp. were used as roofing thatch and wall fill. Cordage was made from bark of dogwood (*Swida sericea*) and juniper, while fibers were extracted from stems of milkweed (*Asclepias* spp.), dogbane (*Apocynum* spp.), and nettle (*Urtica* spp.). A number of yellow composites, such as the beggers ticks (*Bidens* spp.) from llanos and cultivated fields, provided colorful dyes. The various oaks were sources of firewood for long-lasting cooking and warming fires. Other woods, such as poplars (*Populus* spp.) and juniper, were used for quick fires. "Chopeke" (resin sticks) were made from dead pine trees of the ponderosa group (*Pinus ponderosa*, *P. engelmannii*, and *P. arizonica*). These trees may have died due to natural causes (e.g., lightning) or due to humans girdling the trunk, which would encourage the buildup of large amounts of resin. Bathing and washing employed the sudsy extracts from the roots of the buffalo gourd (*Cucurbita foetidissima*). Worked pine cones from the ponderosa group were used to comb the hair.

BARRANCAN OAK WOODLAND

The species of oaks in this woodland include *Quercus chihuahuensis*, *Q. arizonica*, *Q. tuberculata*, *Q. viminea*, *Q. toumeyi*, and *Q. albocincta*. Various magueys (*Agave polianthiflora* and *A. multifilifera*), yucca

(*Yucca schottii*), and beargrass (*Dasylirion leiophyllum*) are scattered throughout. There are many plants and animals in the upper levels of this zone that are common to the Pine-Oak Forest, but densities are lower.

Hunting quail and gathering edible plants such as acorns (*Quercus toumeyi*) and a small maguey (*Agave polianthiflora*) occurred in this zone. Agricultural production was carried out by slash and burn techniques. After 2 to 3 years of growing maize, beans, and squash (similar to those types raised in the Pine-Oak Forest zone), the field was abandoned and allowed to regenerate. Other edible plants cultivated in this zone included *chayotes* (*Sechium edule*) and the *chia* seeds of *Hyptis suaveolens*. The useful anthropogenic plants and animals taken from the fields in this zone were similar to those in the Pine-Oak Forest.

Wild medicinal herbs gathered from this area included "pipichowe" (*Acourtia* spp.), *gordolobo* (*Gnaphalium* spp.), jimsonweed (*Datura inoxia*), and birthwort (*Aristolochia wrightii*). Weedy medicinal plants were similar to those obtained from fields in the Pine-Oak Forest.

Construction material from this zone included the trunks and springy, slender branches of various oaks (*Quercus* spp.). The decay-resistant leaves of such oaks as *Quercus albocincta* were used as fillers in house walls, and the leaves of palms (*Sabal uresana* and *Erythea aculeata*) served for roof and wall thatch. Cordage was supplied by the leaves of yuccas, beargrass (*Nolina* spp.), and palms, while the hard fibers were extracted from the leaves of maguey and yucca. The most common fuel in this zone was oak. Ashes of the burnt bark of Arizona oak (*Q. arizonica*) were mixed with maize for making tortillas.

A popular dye was derived from the flowers of wild zinnia (*Zinnia angustifolia*). Extracts from the yucca served as a cleansing agent. The yucca and a maguey (*Agave bovicornuta*) were common fish-stunning agents gathered from the oak forest opening.

SHORT TREE FOREST

The Short Tree Forest is characterized by two types of trees: the legume trees of the open slopes (leaves are dropped during the dry season) and the many tropical trees along the permanent streams and rivers.

Doves, coati, and otters were commonly hunted in this region, while fish--stunned by extracts of agave (*Agave vilmoriniana*) and plants from higher zones--were gathered from the rivers during the non-rainy season. "Arí," a scale insect (*Tachardiella fulgens*) deposit, was gathered from the host tree "samó" (*Coursetia glandulosa*), eaten in sauces, used to mend pots, and taken as a stomach and fever medicine. Toward the end of the dry season and into the wet season, various fruits were collected from such trees as wild fig (*Ficus* spp.), wild guava (*Psidium sartorianum*), wild mulberry (*Morus microphylla*), "chúwa" (*Bumelia persimilis*), igualama (*Vitex mollis*), hackberry (*Celtis* spp.), Zingg's cherry (*Prunus ferruginea*), "romate" (*Solanum candidum*), "papache" (*Randia* spp.), and guamúchili (*Pithecellobium dulce*), as were fruits of cacti such as organ-pipe cactus (*Lemaireocereus thurberi*), barrel cactus (*Ferocactus alamosanus*), and pincushion cactus (*Mammillaria* spp.). In the fall, the pungent fruits of wild peppers (*Capsicum annuum* var. *glabriusculum*) were eagerly gathered and used as a flavoring for foods and as a medicine. At the beginning of the growing season young tender leaves, for greens, were gathered from blood-leaf (*Iresine* spp.), kidney-wood (*Eysenhardtia polystachya*), wild mustard (*Thelypodiopsis byei*), and "sewachili" (*Jacobinia candicans*). The dry season was the appropriate time to collect the succulent roots of wild papaya (*Jarilla chocola*), jicama (*Exogonium bracteatum*), and wild kapok (*Ceiba acuminata*).

Agricultural activities were usually concentrated along slopes and arroyos during the winter season, when many families migrated to the lower elevations. Few people remained and cultivated during the hot summer season. The maize races were usually limited to a few barrancan types: *Reventador* (flint) and *Blandito* (white flour). The beans included *Phaseolus vulgaris*. The squashes were usually *Cucurbita mixta* and *chayote* (*Sechium edule*). The edible grain, panic grass (*Panicum sonorum*), and the multipurpose bottle gourd (*Lagenaria siceraria*) were also cultivated in this zone. Edible animals, often trapped or gathered in the fields, included various rodents and insects. Associated anthropogenic edible plants included the leafy greens of goosefoot (*Chenopodium berlandieri*) and green pigweed (*Amaranthus hybridus*), as well as the tender leaves and pods of "tabachin" (*Caesalpinia pulcherrima*).

Many wild plants were gathered and used in treating various ailments. Bark of *copalquin* (*Hintonia* spp.) and the herbs of snakeherb (*Zornia* spp.) and lemon herb (*Pectis stenophylla*) are effective in treating fevers and colds. Toothaches were alleviated with the bark and juice of wild croton (*Croton* sp.), ocotillo (*Parthenium stramonium*), and ocotillo tree (*Fouquieria macdougalii*). The juices of *sangre de drago* (*Jatropha* spp.) and *copal* (*Bursera* spp.) proved useful in treating wounds. Stomach disorders were alleviated with an infusion of wormseed (*Chenopodium ambrosioides*).

Strong woods from *palo de asta* (*Cordia sonorae*), mulberry, canyon sycamore (*Platanus wrightii*), "amapa" (*Tabebuia* spp.), guasima (*Guazuma ulmifolia*), and various legume trees such as acacia (*Acacia* spp.) were commonly employed in the construction of houses and the manufacture of wooden items. Reeds (*Phragmites australis*) and "otate" (*Arundinaria longifolia*) were made into mats, walls, and roof thatch. Cordage was derived from various vines, including snake vine (*Serjania mexicana*).

For long-lasting, hot-cooking fuels, various legume trees (*Lysiloma* spp., *Acacia* spp., *Mimosa* spp., and *Pithecellobium dulce*) as well as hardwoods such as "bebelama" (*Sassafridium macrophyllum*) were employed. For fast fires or for kindling, softwooded trees such as morning-glory tree (*Ipomoea arborescens*) and wild fig (*Ficus* spp.) were burned. Pitch sticks for starting fires and for lighting were made from resinous pine trees found along the rivers after they had been carried down the streams from the high country. Cleansing agents were derived from a maguey (*Agave vilmoriniana*) and the ocotillo tree. Sudsing and fish-stunning plants included poisonarrow bushes (*Sapium biloculare* and *Sebastiana pavoniana*). Popular dyes were made from brazil wood (*Haematoxylon brasiletto*) and indigo bush (*Indigofera* spp.). The bristly fruit of *cardon* cactus (*Pachycereus pecten-aboriginum*) served as a hair comb.

SUMMARY

The above account incorporates some of the common plants used in everyday activities and is arranged by vegetation zone, type of use, and season. Human activities associated with plants and animals varied as to method of exploitation, intensity of interaction, season of the year, and availability in fresh or preserved form. These factors influenced not only the people with respect to the quality of the product they used, but also the biological resources with respect to their populations' growth and maintenance. This system is interesting in that the steep ecological gradient allowed for the preferential choice of resources for exploitation in order to meet varying demands brought on by cultural and environmental restrictions. The wild resources reacted by increasing or decreasing in availability and abundance as a consequence of hunting and gathering. The anthropogenic resources in habitats mediated by human activities usually increased in density and lasted over a longer season. These two types of resources may have been considered to be in the public domain, in that anyone could collect them for personal use. Cultivated resources, on the other hand, resulted from the efforts of individuals or families; only they would have had the right to exploit these plants. Therefore, the pressure placed on the public versus private resources would be different and could result in differential influences on those plants and animals.

Further details on the specific plants and animals mentioned above, as well as other biotic resources and associated human activities, can be found in Bennett and Zingg (1935); Bye (1976, 1979, 1981); Bye, Burgess, and Mares (1975); Gentry (1942, 1963); Mares (1982); and Pennington (1963). Archaeological references (Ascher and Clune 1960; Clune 1960; Cutler 1960; Jones 1933; Zingg 1940) and historical sources (Lumholtz 1902; Safford n.d.; *Relaciones Topográficas* 1777) provide evidence for some continuity over time for the interactions between the biological elements of this region and its people.

118

ENDNOTES

1. In order to save space, only common names are used for most of the animals. Spanish and Tarahumara names, along with their scientific names, are used for the plants because of their greater diversity and the lack of English common names. Tarahumara words are given in quotation marks rather than the conventional italics.

2. Common species of pines include *Pinus arizonica*, *P. ayacahuite*, *P. chihuahuana*, *P. durangensis*, *P. engelmannii*, *P. leiophylla*, and *P. ponderosa*.

3. Common species of oaks include *Quercus arizonica*, *Q. cocolobaefolia*, *Q. crassifolia*, *Q. depressipes*, *Q. durifolia*, *Q. hypoleucoides*, *Q. microphylla*, *Q. oblongifolia*, *Q. omissa*, *Q. rugosa*, and *Q. sideroxyla*.

REFERENCES CITED

Ascher, R., and F. J. Clune, Jr.
1960   Waterfall Cave, Southern Chihuahua, Mexico. American Antiquity 26(2):270-274.

Basauri, C.
1929   Monografía de los Tarahumaras. México, D.F.: Talleres Gráficos de la Nación.

Bennett, W. C., and R. M. Zingg
1935   The Tarahumara: An Indian Tribe of Northern Mexico. Chicago: University of Chicago Press. (New edition with color photographs by L. G. Verplancken, S.J., published by Rio Grande Press, Inc., Glorieta, New Mexico, 1976).

Bye, R. A., Jr.
1976   The Ethnoecology of the Tarahumara of Chihuahua, Mexico. Unpublished Ph.D. Thesis (Biology), Harvard University, Cambridge, Massachusetts.

1979   Incipient Domestication of Mustards in Northwest Mexico. Kiva 44(2-3):237-256.

1981   Quelites--Ethnoecology of Edible Greens--Past, Present, and Future. Journal of Ethnobiology 1(1):109-123.

1983   Vegetation and Soils. In: E. R. Stoddard, R. L. Nostrand, and J. P. West, eds., Borderland Sourcebook: A Guide to the Literature on Northern Mexico and the American Southwest, pp. 98-104. Norman, Oklahoma: University of Oklahoma Press.

Bye, R. A., Jr.; D. Burgess; and A. Mares Trías
    1975   Ethnobotany of the Western Tarahumara of Chihuahua, Mexico.
            I. Notes on the Genus *Agave*. Harvard University, Botanical
            Museum Leaflets 24(5):85-112.

Clune, D.
    1960   Textiles and Matting from Waterfall Cave, Chihuahua.
            American Antiquity 26(2):274-277.

Cutler, H.
    1960   Cultivated Plant Remains from Waterfall Cave, Chihuahua.
            American Antiquity 26(2):277-279.

Gentry, H. S.
    1942   Rio Mayo Plants (A Study of the Flora and Vegetation of the
            Valley of the Rio Mayo, Sonora). Carnegie Institution of
            Washington, Publication 527.

    1963   The Warihio Indians of Sonora-Chihuahua: An Ethnographic
            Survey. Anthropological Papers, No. 65, Bureau of American
            Ethnology, Bulletin 186, pp. 61-144. Washington, D.C.:
            Government Printing Office.

Jones, H.
    1933   Ethnobotanical Laboratory Report No. 59 (Robert M. Zingg,
            Northern Mexico in Region of Tarahumare Indians) Manuscript,
            University of Michigan, Museum of Anthropology.

Llaguno, R. J.
    1971   Change in the Tarahumara Family: The Influence of the
            Railroad. Unpublished M.A. Thesis, Department of Sociology,
            Louisiana State University.

Lumholtz, C.
    1902   Unknown Mexico: A Record of Five Years' Exploration among
            the Tribes of the Western Sierra Madre; in the Tierra
            Caliente of Tepic and Jalisco; and among the Tarascos of
            Michoacan. Vols. I and II. New York: Charles Scribner's
            Sons.

Mares Trías, A.
    1982   Ralámuli Nu'tugala Go'ame (Comida de los Tarahumaras en
            Tarahumara del Oeste de Bacusínare, mpio. de Guazapares,
            Chihuahua, y en Español). In collaboration with D. Burgess
            and R. Bye. Chihuahua: Don Burgess McGuire.

Pennington, C. W.
    1963   The Tarahumar of Mexico: Their Environment and Material
            Culture. Salt Lake City: University of Utah Press.

Relaciones Topográficas de Pueblos de México
   1777   Relaciones Topográficas de Pueblos de México. Biblioteca
           Nacional, Madrid, Ms. 2449. (For further details, see Bye
           and Pennington references.)

Safford, W. E.
   n.d.   Edward Palmer, Botanical Explorer. Unpublished manuscript,
           Department of Botany, Smithsonian Institution.

Schmidt, R. H., Jr.
   1975   The Climate of Chihuahua, Mexico. Technical Reports on the
           Meteorology and Climatology of Arid Regions, No. 23.
           University of Arizona, Institute of Atmospheric Physics.

Zingg, R. M.
   1940   Report on Archaeology of Southern Chihuahua. Contributions
           of the University of Denver, Center of Latin American
           Studies, No. 1. Denver, Colorado: The University of Denver.

ETHNOGRAPHIC ANALYSIS
OF A 12TH CENTURY FEMALE MUMMY
FROM CHIHUAHUA, MEXICO

Judith Strupp Green

In the autumn of 1966, according to their account, two men dug a mat-wrapped, female mummy out of a cave floor in a remote region of Chihuahua, Mexico. They transported it (and a fragmentary mummy of a child, found in the same cave) to the United States where the mummies eventually came into the care of the San Diego Museum of Man. The mummies' misadventures, from discovery to museum laboratory, are described elsewhere (Tyson, this volume).

This paper is concerned with the overall appearance of the female mummy--especially the clothing, ornamentation, and burial accoutrements. Where applicable, comparisons will be made with similar ethnological, ethnohistorical, and archaeological descriptions from the immediate and surrounding areas.

The mummy was discovered in a cave in southwestern Chihuahua (see Tyson, Figure 2, this volume). Nearby towns are Loreto and Santa Ana. The cave was described as "a hollow in the hill" and extended back from the opening approximately 9 meters. This region is defined as Upland Country (Figure 1) by Pennington (1963), who describes it as a rolling plateau, averaging about 2,000 meters in altitude with many narrow V-shaped valleys. Pine species are common, with mixed pine and oak stands on upland valley slopes, and plants of the amaryllis family, including *Agave* spp., and the lily family, including *Nolina* spp. and *Dasylirion* spp., on the open slopes of the canyons (Pennington 1963:33-35; see also Bye, Ethnoecological Notes for Southwestern Chihuahua, this volume).

In this same region, in the 1930s, Howard Scott Gentry (1963:124) visited a remarkably similar cave in the Sierra Canelo west of Loreto and Santa Ana. Both caves had been invaded by grazing cattle which had trampled some of the burials. The dead were wrapped in mats or baskets of palm leaves.

At the time of earliest Spanish contact, in the late 16th century, historical sources indicate that the Varohio (or Warihio) Indians occupied the area of the cave, although the Tarahumara were reported in the region later (Figure 2). There is considerable controversy over the distinctness of the Tarahumara and Varohio, which Hinton explores in his preface to Gentry's study of the Varohio (1963:65-68). For the purposes of ethnographic comparison, I have included material from the Tarahumara and Tepehuan Indian ethnographies as well as the neighboring Cahita groups (Yaqui and Mayo Indians) which Sauer (1935:10) thought were linguistically related.

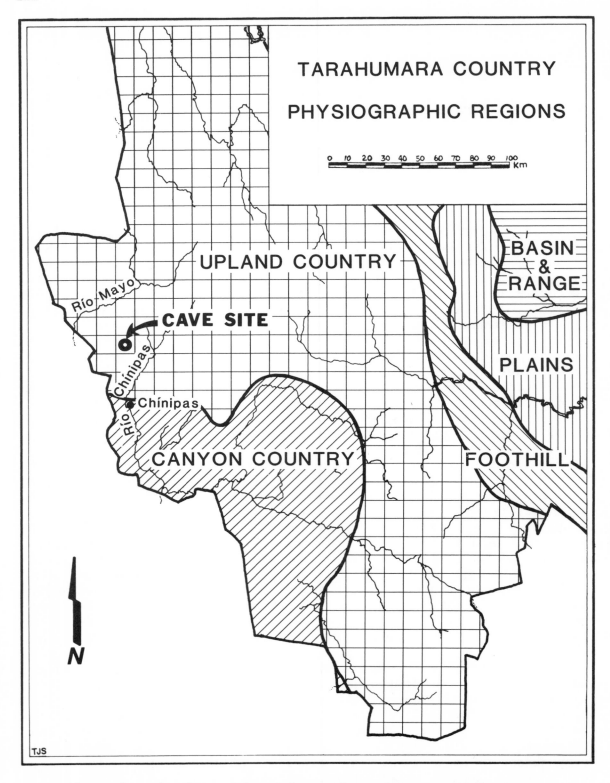

Figure 1.   Physiographic regions of southwestern Chihuahua
(after Pennington 1963:Map 4).

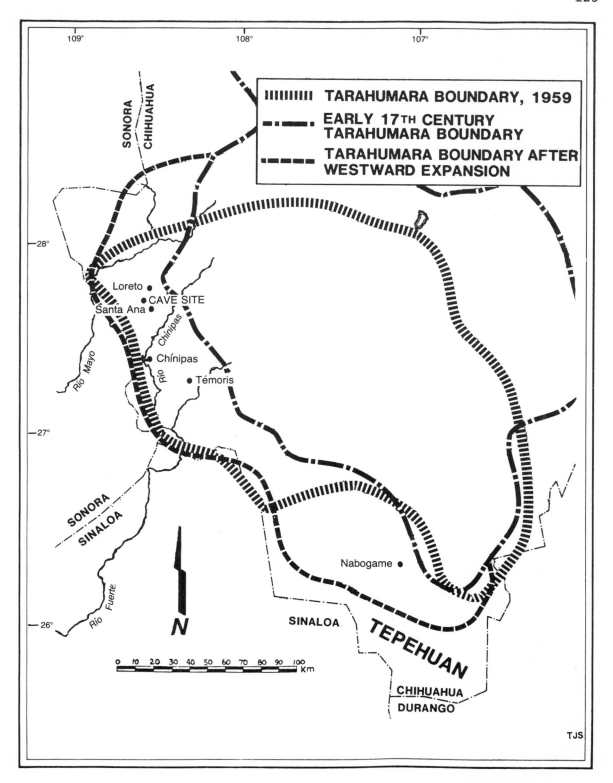

Figure 2. Tarahumara territory showing location of cave
and Tarahumara boundaries (after Pennington 1963:Maps 1 and 2).

APPEARANCE

An initial impression of the mummy is of a dark-haired person contorted into a tightly flexed, fetal position, lying on the side (Figure 3). Delicate hands protrude from between the legs; the feet are crossed. The lower part of the face is compressed. Physical studies have revealed the mummy to be a pregnant female, about 15 years old, who may have been in premature labor at time of death (Pinter, this volume; Luibel-Hulen, this volume; Alcauskas, this volume).

As to the tightly flexed position of the body, the archaeological literature for this area reveals that flexed burial in a cave cist or a pit is well documented. According to Gentry (1963:124), the Varohio bury their dead, but in the past, "...the dead were trussed up into large baskets made of palm leaves or of *carrizo* and cached in caves, the openings of which were walled shut with stones." Gentry (1963:124) visited such a cave in the Sierra Canelo:

> Cattle had gained entrance to the large half-open cavern and had eaten many of the burial baskets and trampled and broken the bones of the dead....The following articles were collected among the scattered bones: crude shell beads, two samples of "petate" baskets...burned bone, a sherd, and hulls of acorns. These last were provisions for the dead and had been placed inside the baskets.

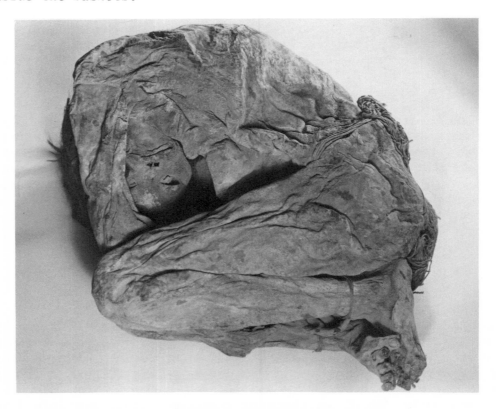

Figure 3. The adolescent female mummy.

Zingg (1940:7) described an excavation of ancient cave burials in the Tarahumara area near Norogachic in southern Chihuahua. He stated:

> ...a hole was dug, averaging 5 feet by 3 feet. This was lined to a height of 8 inches with large thick slabs of pine bark (*Pinus ayahuite* [sic]). In one case this bark floor or lining had been reinforced by an original foundation of saplings. The body was placed in this crypt, which was so small as to make flexing of the knees necessary. Over the top of the pine-bark lining, and enclosing the body, a few saplings were laid to support the roof of heavy white mud, 1 to 3 inches in thickness.

At Waterfall Cave, southwestern Chihuahua, in an area identified at contact with the Tarahumara, archaeologists Ascher and Clune (1960:271) described their findings as "...tightly flexed bodies lying on the side." Lumholtz too, at the turn of the century, found mummies near Nararachic and Aboreachic in Tarahumara country "...bent up and laid on their sides" (1902(I):222).

Today, extended burial in the earth is practiced by the Christian Tarahumara (Bennett and Zingg 1935:237-239), the Mayo (Beals 1945:70), the Yaqui (Beals 1945:78-79), and the Tepehuan (Pennington 1969:156). Bennett and Zingg observed and recorded a Tarahumara cave burial at Quírare. The extended body was placed in a cave where many others had been placed previously. "The mouth of the cave was opened; and the corpse, loosened from its fastenings, was slowly pushed inside. The food, cross, rosary, and hat were put into the cave beside the body.... The mouth of the cave was closed up again with stones and mud" (Bennett and Zingg 1935:237-238). Besides cemetery burial, Basauri (1929:45-46) witnessed two types of cave burial:

> The custom of some is to arrange the cadaver on its back within a cave and to surround it with thorny branches....Immediately, they close the entrance of the cave with rocks and mud. Others dig a grave 30 to 40 centimeters deep within the cave and bury the corpse with a covering layer of pine branches and over this they spread earth, then rocks, and finally a covering of earth. The position of the cadaver, in the cave as in the grave, is with the head toward the east and with the feet in the direction of the west.

MAT SHROUD

According to the discoverers, the mummy was wrapped in a mat of palm sewn with a vine. Although the original mat had disappeared before the mummy was brought to the Museum of Man, examination revealed traces of it in the form of impressions on the mummy's skin (Figure 4). Rubbings taken of these areas revealed a twilled mat pattern which appears to be "over two, under two." A piece of plant material, possibly from the mat, was removed from the mummy's string skirt. It was identified by

Figure 4. Impression of burial mat.

Miller (this volume) as *Phragmites australis*. Gentry (1963:123) reported mat shrouds or baskets in his description of burial caves in
Varohio country (1963:124). Burials in twilled mats were excavated at
Waterfall Cave (Ascher and Clune 1960:271, Figure 3), and in Zingg's excavations near Norogachic (Zingg 1940:10). Twill patterns of "two by
two" or "three by three" were reported from the latter two sites.

Mat wrapping of the dead is very common in Indian Mexico even today
and is reported for the Yaqui, Mayo, Tarahumara, and Tepehuan, as well
as tribes farther south. The twilled palm mat used as a sitting and
sleeping mat is also used for covering the dead. In fact, when Frances
Toor traveled Mexico in the 1920s studying folk art, she recorded the
common colloquialism *se petateó*, translated as "he has taken himself off
in a petate [lit. he wrapped himself in his petate]," to mean someone
has died (Toor 1947:48).

GRAVE AND GRAVE GOODS

The mummy's discoverers described the burial as in a pit approximately 70 cm below the cave floor and lined with layers of burned pine
bark. An ear of yellow corn, about 15 cm in length, was found inside
the space between the mummy's torso and flexed legs, as well as what appeared to be dried berries and acorns. An animal bone (with dried meat
still attached) was also included. Unfortunately, this food-offering
was lost before the mummy reached the Museum of Man.

Although Gentry discovered burial caves in the general area of the
mummy's site, he did not describe the graves. He did mention, however,
burned bone, a potsherd, and acorn hulls having been placed inside the
burial baskets in a cave in the Sierra Canelo, a region occupied by the

Varohio today (Gentry 1963:124). He noted that the modern Varohio put tortillas or other provisions in the grave with the dead for the journey to the afterlife (1963:125).

Zingg (1940:15) discovered pine-bark-lined burials in his excavations near Norogachic in levels he identified with the Basketmaker culture of the early Southwest. In two of these, he found corn near the mouths of the dead. Charcoal in the soil suggested to Zingg (1940:6) that fire may have been used in burial rituals, as the cave did not appear to have been used for habitation.

When the Norwegian explorer-anthropologist Carl Lumholtz visited and studied the Tarahumara in the 1890s, he found the non-Christianized Tarahumaras burying their dead in or just outside caves. In his words (1902(I):383):

> The body is covered with an inch of earth, then with a row of pine or palm sticks put on lengthwise, and over this a layer of earth is spread five or six inches deep. On top of all, stones are thrown. The bodies of grown persons are stretched out to their full length, but with children the knees are generally drawn up.

Lumholtz (1902(I):383-384) found bits of charcoal near skeletons which he exhumed, explaining this by "...the fact that during the first night the mourners keep a fire near the grave, which to-day serves the same purpose as candles." He also stated that three ears of corn, with other grave goods, were placed at the head of the dead person. Gentry (1963: 86) assumed that the prehispanic Varohio did not have maize before the Jesuits arrived.

CLOTHING

The only item of clothing worn by the mummy is a string apron-skirt (Figure 5), which could also be described as a breechclout of plant fiber. In 1934, one of Gentry's informants reported that previously the Varohios had worn only breechclouts (1963:85). Gentry stated that "... naked women were observed in the evening about the house fires near Carimechi. Now the prevailing dress among them is the usual Mexican habit." In the 1930s, the Varohio men along the Río Mayo wore a cotton loincloth and back-cover (Gentry 1963:119). As late as 1961, the more conservative Tarahumara also wore a combination of loincloth and back-cover of cotton (Green 1970:88). In the Tarahumara area, in the presumed late Cave-Dweller levels, Zingg (1940:57) excavated a breechclout woven of plant fibers (including *Agave*) and animal hair. This may be a transitional garment between string apron and cotton loincloth (Green 1971:117).

String aprons (Figure 6) have been identified in many archaeological sites in the Southwest (Guernsey and Kidder 1921:46, Plate 16; Haury 1934:63-64, Plate 40; 1950:429, Plates 40-41; and Martin et al. 1952: 325, Figure 127). Zingg (1940:20) described the string apron of a female child mummy from a cave near Norogachic in southern Chihuahua:

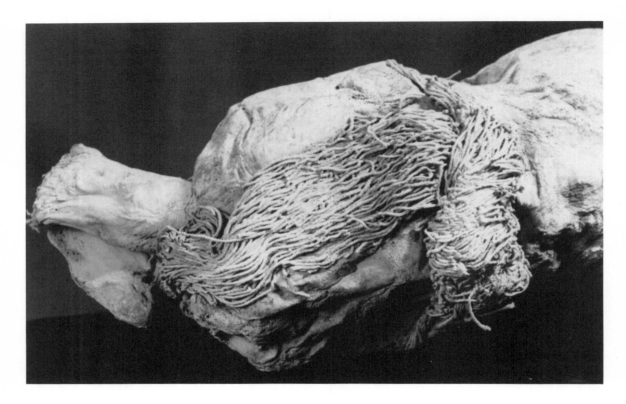

Figure 5. String apron-skirt.

The garment hung from the waist by a cord of three strings
of spun pita fiber (*Agave* sp.). These waist fibers also served
to hold the 34 similar strings of the body of the apron by
means of twine-weaving them with the three strings of the waist
cord. The resultant down-hanging ends of each of the 34
strings are twisted together forming a single two-ply cord.

Dorris Clune (1960:275) described a similar string apron of two-ply
Apocynum yarn from a burial at Waterfall Cave within the present
Tarahumara habitat. String aprons have also been reported for the
neighboring areas of Río Zape, Durango, and Candelaria Cave, Coahuila
(Johnson 1971:Table 2).

The breechclout or string apron on the Chihuahuan mummy appears to
be more ample than many of the others described. Although the frontal
attachment cannot be seen because of the tightly flexed body, it is
clear that about 122 cords were attached to a waistband of 17 cords,
passed through the legs and under the waist cords at the back, then
tucked under once again. The cords are all S-doubled yarns of cotton,
kapok, or *Apocynum* but probably not *Agave*, according to the identification by John Strother (personal communication, 1981) of the University
Herbarium, University of California, Berkeley. Miller (this volume)
gives a tentative identification of the fiber as a species of *Apocynum*.

Cotton (*Gossypium*) was reported by Gentry (1963:87) as cultivated by
the Varohio in two varieties, one a brownish fiber and the other, white

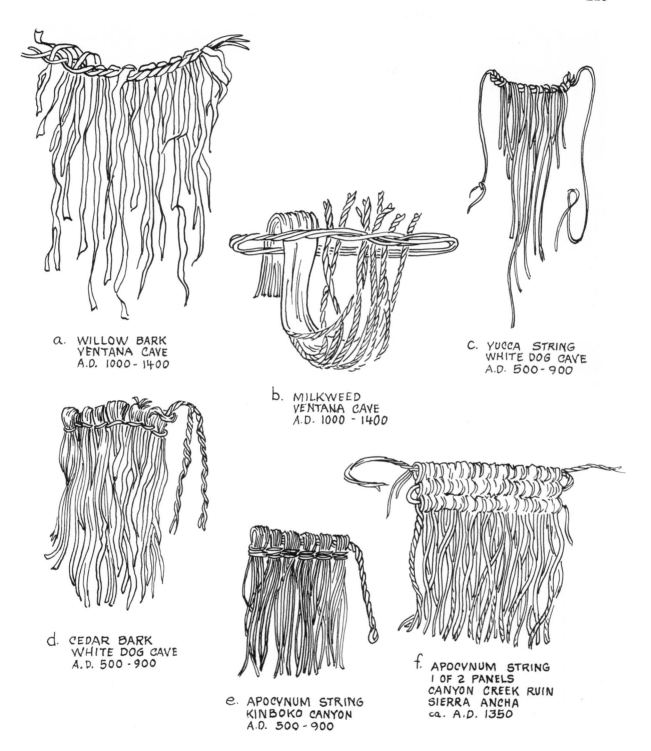

a. WILLOW BARK
VENTANA CAVE
A.D. 1000-1400

b. MILKWEED
VENTANA CAVE
A.D. 1000-1400

c. YUCCA STRING
WHITE DOG CAVE
A.D. 500-900

d. CEDAR BARK
WHITE DOG CAVE
A.D. 500-900

e. APOCYNUM STRING
KINBOKO CANYON
A.D. 500-900

f. APOCYNUM STRING
1 OF 2 PANELS
CANYON CREEK RUIN
SIERRA ANCHA
ca. A.D. 1350

Figure 6. String skirts from Arizona sites (a,b after Haury 1950:
Plates 40,41; c-e after Guernsey and Kidder 1921:Plate 16;
f after Haury 1934:Plate 40), drawing by Barton A. Wright.

130

and long-stapled; it was formerly used by them for weaving blankets and clothing. Kapok (*Ceiba acuminata*) was also found in the area, its corms and seeds used for food. No mention was made of the Varohio (past or present) using it in weaving. An 18th century Franciscan priest at Batopilillas reported that the Tarahumara there used kapok fiber for making skirts, belts, or ribbons (Pennington 1963:205). *Apocynum* used for textiles and cordage has been identified from several archaeological sites (O'Neale 1948; Clune 1960:274). More common in the ethno-historical accounts at early contact was the mention of clothing of pita, generally interpreted as *Agave*.

While certainly the string apron-skirt was used as a garment before the conquest in this area of Mexico, the Spanish accounts are somewhat unclear about the nature of the garments women wore at the time of first contact. It is possible that they wore woven pita skirts or coverings over or instead of the string apron, as Neuman wrote that in the 17th century women were clad to the heels (Pennington 1963:208).

The existence of a maguey fiber breechclout as a burial garment should be mentioned here. During the 1930s, the Yaqui and Mayo to the north and west of the Varohio and Tarahumara used a maguey fiber breechclout as part of the burial costume. Among the Mayo, the deceased was given the "cord of the dead," described as a "...cord and breechclout made of domesticated maguey fiber. It is placed on both male and female, adult and child, over the ordinary clothing. The ends of the breechclout, which are passed over the belt or cord, extend down to the feet between the legs...." (Beals 1945:68). "Among the Yaqui, the body of a married person...is dressed with a cord about the waist and a breechclout...the ends of which reach to the feet" (Beals 1945:77).

The Tarahumara and the Varohio make cordage from *Agave* fiber. The Tarahumara roll the fiber on the thigh, generally considered to be the most ancient manner of spinning and plying (Pennington 1963:203). The Tepehuan also make cordage of *Agave*, rolling it on the thigh for thin cord and using the Spanish-derived *tarabilla* for heavier rope. Zingg (1940:56) found spindles at several sites. These could have been used to spin or ply maguey and other plant fiber yarns in a manner similar to that of the present-day Otomi Indians of Hidalgo.

ADORNMENTS

The mummy's total ornamentation, other than questioned body painting, consists of two anklets and one wooden earplug. The anklets (Figure 7) consist of fine brown cotton strings (*Gossypium*, identified by Miller, this volume) wrapped around each ankle and knotted at the end. One string is wrapped six times around the left ankle; the other, seven times around the right.

Lumholtz reports that several mummies from Cave Valley in north-western Chihuahua wore plaited anklets of plant fiber which "...crumbled into dust when touched" (Lumholtz 1902(I):72). For dancing, the Varohio men wore the *chairigora*, an anklet made of a string of lepidopterous cocoon sacks (Gentry 1963:119). Possibly, the cotton ankle cords had a ritual significance. In a burial ceremony of the Nahuatl-speaking

Figure 7. String anklets.

Indians of Nayarit, the shaman divided white cotton thread among members of the deceased's family; this was to be worn around the neck for one year (Lumholtz 1902(I):483). There is no record of Tarahumara, Tepehuan, Yaqui, or Mayo using ankle cords, although the Huichol to the south and west use beaded anklets.

The ear ornament (Figure 8) is a simple wooden plug, 5 mm in diameter and 18 mm long, inserted through a hole in the earlobe. The plug may be a device to maintain the opening in the lobe, rather than a true ornament. Anderson (1888:11) reported a female mummy from the eastern side of the Sierra Madre, about 320 km south of Deming, New Mexico, with a piece of hollow reed approximately 10 mm in diameter and 40 mm long in each ear. Zingg (1940:51-52) describes an ear-pendant consisting of a worked piece of pearly oyster shell suspended from a string of disc beads made from the shell of a marine bivalve. A large glass bead strung with the shell gives a post-Spanish age. Lumholtz (1902(I):151) illustrated an ear ornament made of a triangular piece of shell attached to a string of beads and commonly worn by Tarahumara women at the turn of the century.

HAIRDRESS

Two fragmentary hairbands of twisted fiber (Figure 9) at the back of the mummy's head appear to have served as "rats" or foundations for

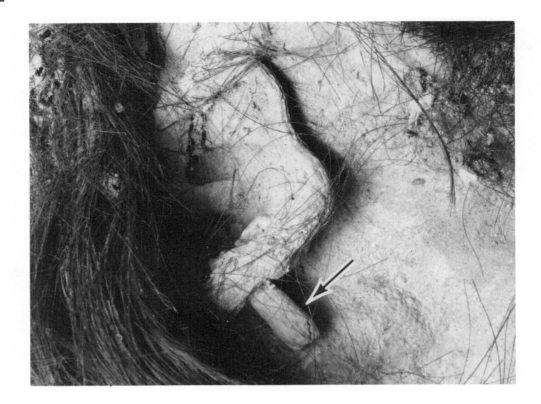

Figure 8. Wooden ear ornament.

braided and twisted hair (Figure 10). The hairbands are made of coarse 2-ply, Z-twist cord, each ply of which is S-twist. The fiber has been identified as *Nolina* (Miller, this volume), a genus common to the region and widely used for baskets by the Varohio (Gentry 1963:115) and the Tarahumara (Pennington 1963:200).

The archaeological finds discussed in this paper do not mention hairdress. The ethnographic reports for the Tarahumara are vague, specifying only that women wore their hair either long or braided (Pennington 1963:213). Pieces of palm which may have been used as hairbands were found at Waterfall Cave. They were described only as three-strand braids of palm frond (Clune 1960:275).

Even today, headbands prepared from *Nolina* are worn (Pennington 1963:204), and Lumholtz (1902(I):150) found Indians at the turn of the century using palm as one of the fibers to tie the hair:

> The hair, when not worn loose, is held together with a home-woven ribbon, or a piece of cotton cloth rolled into a band; or with a strip palm leaf. Often men and women gather the hair in the back of the head, and men may also make a braid of it.

The use of palm or vines as a foundation for a woman's elaborate hairdress is known from some other parts of Mexico. It is found among the Huaxtec of Tamaletón, San Luis Potosí (Cordry and Cordry 1968:Plate 87), and it is apparently ancient in that area.

Figure 9. Hairbands at back of head.

Figure 10. Posterior view showing reconstruction of hairdress
(drawing by Barton A. Wright).

BODY PAINT

The mummy's skin has a patchy red appearance as if painted or stained by some material. A bright light shone on the interior areas, which were presumably somewhat protected from the soil, shows a more even red on the legs and arms. Whether this coloring is from soil staining or from purposeful body painting is not known.

In modern times, the Tarahumara have used body paint for ceremonies (Bennett and Zingg 1935:313); red ocher is widely available in the area (Pennington 1963:218). Gentry (1963:119) reported that in the past the Varohio warriors were accustomed to painting their faces before going to battle. In examining the skeletal material recovered by Lumholtz, Hrdlička (1901:721) found no paint or stain on the Tarahumara skeletons; red coloring was found, however, on a skeleton from the Tepehuan region to the south. Hrdlička (1901:703) was of the opinion that the pigment was probably "...applied to the surface of the bones as paint and subsequently penetrated into their various crevices...."

CONCLUSION

The radiocarbon dating of this mummy between A.D. 1040 and 1260 (Tyson, this volume) predates the earliest ethnohistorical dates for the area by at least four centuries. Therefore, a firm cultural affiliation cannot be established, other than that of the Varohio who occupied the region of the burial cave at contact. In the 1930s, Gentry recorded 18 families of Varohio at Loreto and 15 families at Santa Ana (1963:76), the two localities closest to the cave. Controversy still exists as to whether the Varohio are a distinct people or a subgroup of the Tarahumara (Gentry 1963:67).

The archaeological evidence demonstrates great similarity in burial customs between this mummy and those found by Zingg near Norogachic. His finds and the mummy under discussion were both excavated from pine-bark-lined cave floor cists, wrapped in twilled mats, and wearing string apron-skirts of plant fiber. The presence of corn (presumed from the testimony of the finders in this case) and the evidence of fire also link these burials. Additional similarities include the presence of other foods with the burial and the flexed position of the body. Controlled excavations and accurate descriptions of the burials in this region would make it possible to define the nature of the burial complex more precisely. The presence of well preserved mummies documented from this area, with intact burial goods and clothing, is a research opportunity which should not be missed by archaeologists.

The foregoing description tends to give an incomplete view of the mummy as a dry collection of separate "traits," when in fact she was once a living human being. Barton Wright's drawing of the adolescent female (Figure 11) expands our vision. It recreates the young Indian woman at the threshold of adulthood and in the process of creating a new life before both were prematurely ended.

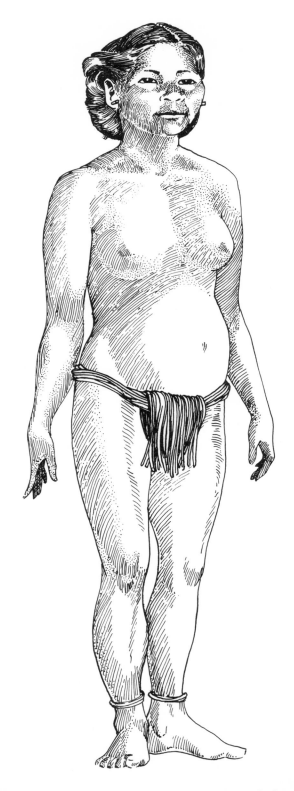

Figure 11. Artist's reconstruction of the adolescent female
(drawing by Barton A. Wright).

REFERENCES CITED

Anderson, Winslow
    1888   A Description of the Desiccated Human Remains in the
            California State Mining Bureau. California State Mining
            Bureau, Bulletin 1. Sacramento.

Ascher, Robert, and Francis J. Clune, Jr.
    1960   Waterfall Cave, Southern Chihuahua, Mexico. American
            Antiquity 26(2):270-274.

Basauri, Carlos
    1929   Monografía de los Tarahumaras. México, D.F.: Talleres
            Gráficos de la Nación.

Beals, Ralph L.
    1945   The Contemporary Culture of the Cahita Indians. Bureau of
            American Ethnology, Bulletin 142. Washington, D.C.:
            Government Printing Office.

Bennett, Wendell C., and Robert M. Zingg
    1935   The Tarahumara: An Indian Tribe of Northern Mexico.
            Chicago: University of Chicago Press. (New edition with
            color photographs by L. G. Verplancken, S.J., published by
            Rio Grande Press, Inc., Glorieta, New Mexico, 1976).

Clune, Dorris
    1960   Textiles and Matting from Waterfall Cave, Chihuahua.
            American Antiquity 26(2):274-277.

Cordry, Donald, and Dorothy Cordry
    1968   Mexican Indian Costumes. Austin: University of Texas Press.

Gentry, Howard Scott
    1963   The Warihio Indians of Sonora-Chihuahua: An Ethnographic
            Survey. Anthropological Papers, No. 65, Bureau of American
            Ethnology, Bulletin 186, pp. 61-144. Washington, D. C.:
            Government Printing Office.

Green, Judith Strupp
    1970   Changes in Tarahumara Women's Work from Prehistoric Times to
            the Present. M.A. Thesis, Department of Anthropology, Tulane
            University. New Orleans, Louisiana.

    1971   Archaeological Chihuahuan Textiles and Modern Tarahumara
            Weaving. Ethnos 36:115-130. Stockholm: National Museum of
            Ethnography.

Guernsey, Samuel James, and Alfred Vincent Kidder
    1921   Basket-Maker Caves of Northeastern Arizona: Report on the
            Explorations, 1916-17. Papers of the Peabody Museum of
            American Archaeology and Ethnology 8(2). Cambridge,
            Massachusetts: Harvard University.

Haury, Emil W.
    1934   The Canyon Creek Ruin and the Cliff Dwellings of the Sierra
            Ancha. Medallion Papers 14. Globe, Arizona: Gila Pueblo.

    1950   The Stratigraphy and Archaeology of Ventana Cave, Arizona.
            Tucson: University of Arizona Press, and Albuquerque:
            University of New Mexico Press.

Hrdlička, Aleš
    1901   A Painted Skeleton from Northern Mexico, with Notes on Bone
            Painting among the American Aborigines. American
            Anthropologist (n.s.) 3(4):701-725.

Johnson, Irmgard Weitlaner
    1971   Basketry and Textiles. In: G. F. Ekholm and I. Bernal,
            eds., Archaeology of Northern Mesoamerica, Part I, pp.
            297-321. Handbook of Middle American Indians, Vol. 10.
            Austin: University of Texas Press.

Lumholtz, Carl
    1902   Unknown Mexico: A Record of Five Years' Exploration among
            the Tribes of the Western Sierra Madre; in the Tierra
            Caliente of Tepic and Jalisco; and among the Tarascos of
            Michoacan. Volumes I and II. New York: Charles Scribner's
            Sons.

Martin, Paul S.; John B. Rinaldo; Elaine Bluhm; Hugh C. Cutler; and
    Roger Grange, Jr.
    1952   Mogollon Cultural Continuity and Change: The Stratigraphic
            Analysis of Tularosa and Cordova Caves. Fieldiana:
            Anthropology 40. Chicago: Chicago Natural History Museum.

O'Neale, Lila M.
    1948   Textiles of Pre-Columbian Chihuahua. Contributions to
            American Anthropology and History 9(45):95-161. Carnegie
            Institute of Washington, Publication 574, Washington, D.C.

Pennington, Campbell W.
    1963   The Tarahumar of Mexico: Their Environment and Material
            Culture. Salt Lake City: University of Utah Press.

    1969   The Tepehuan of Chihuahua: Their Material Culture. Salt
            Lake City: University of Utah Press.

138

Sauer, Carl
    1935   Aboriginal Population of Northwestern Mexico. Ibero-
            Americana 10. Berkeley: University of California Press.

Toor, Frances
    1947   A Treasury of Mexican Folkways. New York: Crown Publishers.

Zingg, Robert M.
    1940   Report on Archaeology of Southern Chihuahua. Contributions
            of the University of Denver, Center of Latin American
            Studies, No. 1. Denver, Colorado: The University of Denver.

ESTUDIOS INTERDISCIPLINARIOS
EN DOS MOMIAS
PROVENIENTES DE CHIHUAHUA, MÉXICO
Resumen en Español

Jorge Felipe Cárdenas

El presente estudio tiene como objeto divulgar una serie de datos referentes a dos momias encontradas en el estado de Chihuahua, y que fueron obtenidos por varios investigadores en diversas disciplinas. Así pues, este artículo es un resumen general que, dadas las limitaciones del espacio disponible, busca sintetizar de la mejor manera los informes que aquí se publican.

Contrariamente a lo que podría pensarse, la historia de estos dos especímenes ha sido bastante accidentada. Primero, no fueron adquiridos mediante excavaciones arqueológicas sistemáticas sino que, por el contrario, fueron descubiertos por dos jóvenes aventureros intrigados por los rumores sobre cuerpos indígenas momificados en las aisladas cuevas de la Sierra Madre Occidental. Acompañados por un caporal y varios indígenas y, pasadas inumerables peripecias, localizaron una cueva donde estaban enterradas las dos momias objeto de este trabajo. Aparentemente había otras más que no pudieron transportar por la dificultad que representaba su movilización en terreno tan quebrado. Una vez en los Estados Unidos, guardaron las momias en un garaje donde permanecieron olvidadas 14 años hasta que una aterrorizada dama las encontró cuando se dedicaba a organizar ese lugar. Después de dar aviso a la oficina del alguacil de policía del condado de San Diego, las momias pasaron a los laboratorios del Museo del Hombre de esa ciudad donde permanecen hasta el día de hoy para adelantar diversos estudios, en común acuerdo con el Instituto Nacional de Antropología e Historia de México.

El despliegue noticioso por los medios de comunicación hizo que los descubridores relataran su historia a las autoridades del museo, describiendo que la cueva tenía varios fragmentos de cerámica "rojiza y castaño claro con marcas negras". Los restos de una de las momias estaban parcialmente descubiertos y habían sufrido las pisadas del ganado que generalmente se refugiaba allí; pero la segunda momia que encontraron estaba en perfecto estado, envuelta en una estera y enterrada bajo capas de corteza de árbol y tierra, procedimiento característico de la región. En el espacio formado por las piernas flexadas y el torso, había una mazorca y lo que aparentemente eran bayas secas. También encontraron un hueso de animal con la carne adherida aún. Desafortunadamente, todos estos elementos culturales desaparencieron antes de que las momias llegaran al museo. Estudios anteriores han demostrado que, efectivamente, los indígenas enterraban a sus muertos con provisiones para la otra vida y también que los enterraban cubriéndolos con capas de corteza de pino y tierra.

En el suroccidente de los Estados Unidos, (especialmente en el área ocupada por los actuales estados de Utah, Colorado, Arizona y Nuevo México) la momificación siempre se dió como proceso natural y no hay indicios de que se practicara con el propósito específico de preservar los cuerpos. Las condiciones de aridez de esta región, junto con el tipo de suelos y arenas (estas últimas casi indiferenciables de aquellas en Egipto), los enterramientos en cuevas y el tipo de mortaja de fibras vegetales, hicieron posible el desecamiento. Sin embargo, el porcentaje de momias provenientes de esta región es relativamente bajo. Según El-Najjar y Mulinski (1980) el número de momias procedentes de esta área es solamente 43, aun cuando hay otras más que no han sido listadas ni examinadas. La razón para tan bajo número de especímenes en una región donde supuestamente deberían abundar pueden ser diversas pero, básicamente, se tienen en cuenta las siguientes: 1- que se practicara la cremación; 2- que las poblaciones no fueran tan densas como se piensa; y 3- que no siempre se presentaban las condiciones ideales para el desecamiento.

Indudablemente los cuerpos momificados de pasadas poblaciones humanas son un recurso de invaluable información antropológica. Sin embargo, una vez retirados de su ambiente seco, son frágiles y están expuestos a condiciones de laboratorio que pueden causarles daños irreparables. Las autopsias suministran muchísima información, pero con la consecuente pérdida del espécimen. Por esta razón es de primordial importancia que diversos investigadores tengan acceso directo al material, aun cuando nuestro principal interés debe radicar en la conservación de tales muestras.

Las momias provienen de una área cercana a la aldea de Santa Ana, en el municipio de Chinipas, Chihuahua. En un radio de apenas 10km las elevaciones varían entre 700 hasta más de 2000 metros con lo cual se originan diversas zonas ecológicas. Dadas las cortas distancias, estas fueron de fácil acceso para los antiguos indígenas y aun hoy para los actuales tarahumara que habitan la región. Es probable que las poblaciones se movieran hacia las montañas altas durante el verano y, de manera similar, hacia los cañones más bajos durante el invierno. Los suelos se orginan por la degradación de la capa terciaria dominante de roca volcánica, con afloramientos esporádicos de rocas metamórficas y sedimentarias mesozoicas, y por la deposición de materia orgánica producida por los bosques. La vegetación, que corresponde a factores climáticos y topográficos, se puede clasificar en tres zonas:

1- Zona superior, con elevaciones sobre los 1525 metros. En esta zona dominan los bosques de pino y roble.

2- Cañones superiores, con elevaciones entre 915 y 1525 metros, dominados principalmente por bosques de roble.

3- Elevaciones bajas inferiores a 915 metros. Se caracteriza por la presencia de árboles pequeños.

En la primera zona las actividades agrícolas se limitaban a aquellas áreas donde se facilitaba arar el terreno y fertilizarlo con excrementos de murciélago. Las terrazas aluviales de los arroyos también se prestaban para sembrar, y el cultivo básico era naturalmente el maíz en diversas variedades. En la segunda zona se presentó una importante diferencia en la técnica de producción agrícola. La tala y quema de bosque fue característica y, luego de unos tres años de producción de maíz, fríjoles y calabazas, se abandonaban los campos para permitir su regeneración. La tercera zona se caracteriza especialmente por la presencia de plantas leguminosas y árboles tropicales a lo largo de los ríos. Esta variedad ecológica suministraba las condiciones para producir una buena diversidad de alimentos, así como también de plantas medicinales y materiales para la construcción.

Las momias que nos ocupan en este estudio se caracterizan por los siguientes aspectos: el sexo de la niña se determinó mediante observación directa de los genitales externos. Se encuentra flexada (posición fetal) con las piernas hacia el abdomen, la columna recta y el brazo derecho descansando sobre el muslo del mismo costado (Figura 1). La influencia cristiana ha cambiado esta tradicional postura y actualmente los indios entierran a sus muertos en posición extendida. El cuerpo es fragmentario y están ausentes la cabeza, el omoplato izquierdo, la clavícula izquierda, las costillas izquierdas, todo el brazo izquierdo, las vértebras cervicales y torácicas, los metatarsos izquierdos y las falanges de ambos pies. La edad se estimó entre seis meses y un año y medio con base en las medidas tomadas de los huesos largos. En cuanto a patologías, las radiografías mostraron un leve engrosamiento de las diáfisis de los huesos largos con posible periostitis concomitante.

La momia adulta también es de sexo femenino y, al igual que la anterior, está en posición flexada (Figura 2). Es interesante notar que presenta marcas de la estera en que fue envuelta, sobre el brazo y muslo

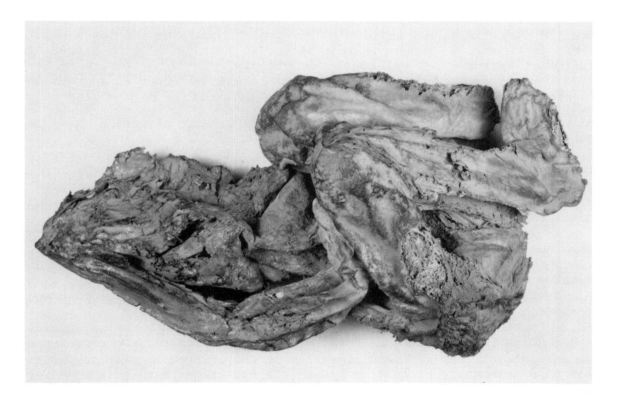

Figura 1. Momia de la niña.

izquierdos, tentativamente identificada como *Phragmites australis* (caña común). Los ojos están abiertos con los globos oculares todavía presentes. Lo más sobresaliente es el hecho de que esta mujer estaba embarazada. El examen radiográfico indicó que el feto se encontraba entre el séptimo y octavo mes de desarrollo, y es muy probable que el trabajo de parto ya se hubiera iniciado, como lo demuestra la superposición de los huesos del cráneo y su localización en la región pélvica. La edad de la madre al momento de morir se ha calculado alrededor de 15 años $\pm$ 36 meses con base en la erupción de la dentadura permanente y la unión incompleta de las crestas ilíacas y los cuerpos vertebrales. Se observó una pequeña región porosa en el occipital que puede deberse a un tumor benigno o a un hematoma subperióstico calcificado. La fecha de radiocarbono para la momia embarazada se calculó en 860 $\pm$ 40 AP (calibrada en 1040-1260 AD).

La determinación del grupo sanguíneo se hizo mediante el método de aglutinación de células mixtas. El resultado fue tipo O, lo cual está de acuerdo con la mayoría de los grupos indígenas de América del Sur y América Central. Otros estudios de grupos sanguíneos en 55 momias provenientes del suroccidente norteamericano han dado porcentajes de 89% tipo O y 11% tipo A. Donald Pate (este volumen) explica en su informe que los pequeños porcentajes de genes A y B en estas poblaciones se introdujeron con los europeos y se encuentran en proporciones más altas del 10% en grupos canadienses y norteamericanos, decreciendo considerablemente hacia el sur.

La escanografía computarizada también juega un papel muy importante en la investigación. Los exámenes radiográficos convencionales suministran la densidad de los tejidos suaves pero, combinados con los análisis escanográficos, se logra una reconstrucción detallada de la estructura anatómica macroscópica del objeto de estudio. Tanto la imagen del tejido óseo como la del tejido suave se forman mediante el uso de una fuente movible de rayos X, un sistema de detección y un computador que analiza la absorción de los rayos.

Algunos de los resultados obtenidos muestran que el cerebro disecado y algunos de los órganos torácicos están presentes, aun cuando estos últimos son indefinibles. Otro dato importante es que la sínfisis púbica está desarticulada. Se ha insinuado que si el parto estaba en proceso, la producción de hormonas podría relajar el cartílago y facilitar la desarticulación; sin embargo, también podría tratarse de un fenómeno postmórtem o de una deformación traumática de la pelvis.

La determinación de la edad al momento de morir, desde el punto de vista histológico, se hizo con base en tres núcleos tomados del aspecto anterior del fémur, cada uno de 3,60mm de diámetro. Cada núcleo se seccionó en el plano transverso al eje longitudinal del fémur, cortándose luego dos secciones de 100 micras de cada núcleo que se observaron bajo el microscopio. Luego se estimaron las edades mediante una fórmula regresiva para cada núcleo y cuyos resultados indican que, efectivamente, la mujer murió antes de cumplir los 20 años de edad. También se determinó que no padecía de enfermedades metabólicas de los huesos.

Otro de los aspectos que se tuvieron en cuenta fue el nivel proteínico y calórico de la mujer embarazada. En realidad, este tipo de información ayuda a explicar las condiciones sociales, políticas y

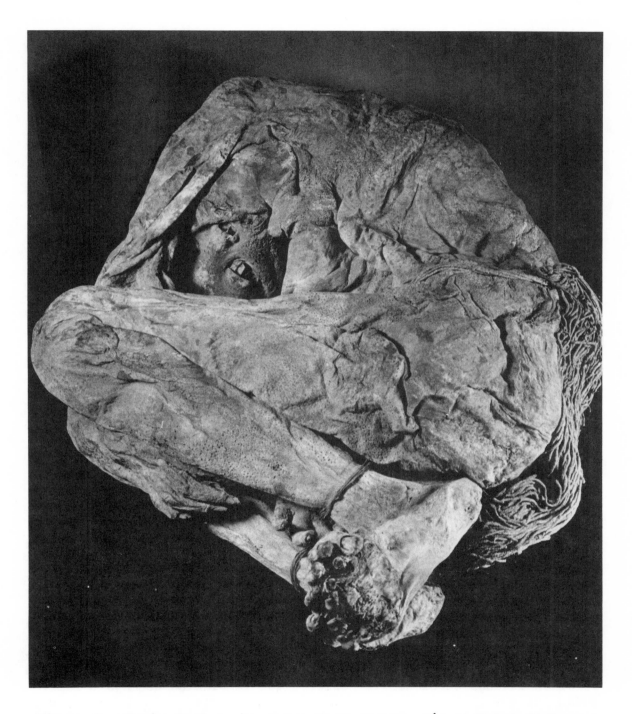

Figura 2. Momia de la mujer embarazada (fotografía de Peter Koeleman reproducida con autorización del *San Diego Union*.)

económicas de los pueblos bajo estudio, como también las diversas afecciones patológicas derivadas de deficiencias nutricionales. Los problemas que pueden presentarse son reacciones inmunológicas deficientes como también procesos anormales de crecimiento y desarrollo. En materiales óseos, las patologías que indican problemas nutricionales son básicamente las líneas de Harris o líneas de crecimiento interrumpido, e hiperostosis porótica o hiperostosis esponjosa. Sin embargo, la deficiencia de proteínas y calorías afecta primeramente aquellos tejidos ricos en proteínas y el cabello es uno de tales tejidos, con altísimos requerimientos metabólicos. El proceso de formación de folículos se distingue por tres fases que son de crecimiento, de involución y de reposo; estas fases se llaman anagenia, catagenia y telogenia y sus frecuencias pueden determinar la presencia de malnutrición. El conteo de folículos anágenos en individuos normalmente nutridos se aproxima entre 80 y 90% y, para el caso de la momia de Chihuahua, el análisis de 93 folículos determinó solamente 18% anágenos. Sin embargo, el estado de gravidez de la mujer justifica la reducción en el número de anágenos, por lo cual se podría considerar un estado de malnutrición aguda en sus primeras fases.

Las causas que originaron la muerte de estos individuos siguen sin determinar a ciencia cierta. Este estudio se realizó mediante el empleo de radiografías, escanografía computarizada y observación directa, y los resultados son apenas tentativos. Las radiografías de la niña muestran cierto engrosamiento del cúbito, radio, tibia y peroné en aquellos lugares donde se depositó material hiperostótico. Se sospecha que puede tratarse de una inflamación de periostio debido a sífilis congénita. Sin embargo, actualmente no existe ningún método mediante el cual se puedan detectar los antígenos del treponema y, por consiguiente, no se puede dar un dictamen final al respecto.

En el caso de la madre, no se han encontrado hasta el momento traumas específicos y se han sugerido dos posibilidades: ruptura de placenta y eclampsia del embarazo. En el primer caso, la ruptura daría origen al parto prematuro y muerte de la madre por hemorragia interna. Como ya se ha visto, la momia presenta desarticulación de la sínfisis púbica y un golpe fuerte pudo ser la causa de este problema. La eclampsia, o toxemia metabólica del embarazo, es común y causa la muerte de la madre y parto prematuro. Generalmente se debe a la presencia de exceso de proteínas serosas en la orina, edema o hipertensión, y el paciente sufre convulsiones y coma.

Otra de las técnicas empleadas en el análisis de las momias fue la escanografía por microscopía electrónica. Esta tiene como característica principal hacer resaltar la topografía de la superficie, y complementa de esta forma las otras técnicas microscópicas. Todas las muestras estudiadas se tomaron de la mujer embarazada. Una de las fibras encontradas parece pertenecer a la estera en que estaba envuelta la momia y tentativamente identificada como *Phragmites australis*. La falda que lleva a la cintura está compuesta de fibras retorcidas. Las secciones transversales estudiadas muestran generalmente el interior homogéneo pero, en algunas ocasiones, se observó que también se asemeja a repliegues. Es muy probable que se trate de alguna especie de *Apocynum*, como el cáñamo o la adelfa. Según los datos de otros investigadores, algunas mujeres andaban desnudas en sus casas y, hasta hace unos 20 años, los hombres tarahumara se ponían un pequeño taparrabo de algodón. Zingg (1940) excavó en esta región un taparrabo fabricado de fibras vegetales (incluyendo *Agave*) y pelos de animal. Este mismo investigador ha descrito otra pequeña falda de cuerdas perteneciente a una momia de la región suroccidental de los Estados Unidos, y varios autores han encontrado prendas semejantes en esta región. En la momia que nos ocupa, es probable que unas 122 cuerdas conforman la falda. Las ajorcas que lleva alrededor de los tobillos son de cuerdas muy finas de algodón. La vincha que lleva en la cabeza se compone de una fibra de superficie acanalada cuidadosamente entretejida. Estas estructuras, junto con los bordes en forma de sierra, son características del género *Nolina*, género este que está presente en la región tarahumara de donde provienen las momias, representado por las especies *Nolina durangensis* y *Nolina matapensis*. Actualmente se usan vinchas fabricadas con estas plantas. También es interesante anotar que algunas cestas de los actuales indios, existentes en el Museo del Hombre, estan fabricadas con fibras que son indiferenciables de la muestra arqueológica.

Para los tarahumara, las enfermedades se dividen en dos categorías: la primera corresponde a aquellas que afectan al espíritu y, la segunda, a las que afectan el cuerpo. Estas últimas se consideran de poca gravedad a menos que hagan de la morada de los espíritus (que es el cuerpo) un lugar inhabitable. Ahora bien, las enfermedades tienen siempre una causa y pueden atribuirse a la negligencia de uno mismo o a otros seres. Por ejemplo, el consumo de alimentos amargos, de maíz tierno o de alimentos con el estómago vacío se cuentan dentro de esta categoría. La complicación en los partos también se considera de este tipo.

En la segunda categoría juega papel importante el "sukúruame" o hechicero. Estos individuos adquieren sus conocimientos por la relación que afirman tener con Dios y el Demonio. Así, pueden causar la enfermedad a una persona con quien no simpatizan y, naturalmente, curar enfermedades causadas por otros hechiceros. Generalmente tienen que ver con aquellas que afectan al espíritu. Existen también otra clase de hechiceros que solamente causan mal.

Los tarahumara practican dos tipos de tratamiento médico. El primero es preventivo, mientras que el segundo es paliativo. Generalmente el tratamiento preventivo es de uso ceremonial y tiene lugar durante el desarrollo de algunas fiestas. Normalmente se entierran las ofrendas junto a la base de una pequeña cruz, y están dedicadas al Demonio para que no cause enfermedades. También es común colocar ciertas plantas a la entrada de las habitaciones o alrededor de los recipientes que contienen tesgüino, para así contrarrestar el poder de los hechiceros y seres malignos. Generalmente son plantas espinosas, como especies de cactos (*Opuntia* spp.) y acacia (*Acacia* spp.), o tambíen chile (*Capsicum annuum*). El tratamiento paliativo puede llevarse a cabo por una persona no especialista, si no se trata de algo grave; por un especialista, si la enfermedad reviste gravedad; y por médicos occidentales, puesto que los tarahumara consideran que éstos también son criaturas del Demonio. Las plantas que se utilizan en las fiestas curativas se emplean como ofrendas o se consumen. Otras se convierten en polvos, inciensos y líquidos, y se esparcen sobre las personas participantes, los campos de

cultivo y los animales. Normalmente los alimentos derivados del maíz
están presentes durante estas ceremonias y el tesgüino, con ciertos adi-
tivos, se considera con propiedades curativas. La corteza seca y pulve-
rizada de ciertos árboles (*Fraxinus* spp. y *Alnus* spp.) se utiliza para
curar animales.

Durante las ceremonias es súmamente importante fumar tabaco. Muchos
tabacos comerciales se emplean en estas ocasiones, aun cuando los indios
prefieren usar tabacos locales. Así pues, hay muchas plantas que consumen tanto los pacientes como los participantes en las ceremonias, todas
las cuales juegan un papel importante en los procesos curativos.

Hay algunas plantas que se conocen con el nombre de "uchurí",
"rikúhuri", "híkuri" y "bakánawi". Los diversos investigadores de esta
región parecen diferir con respecto a las propiedades y circunstancias
en que se aplican y, por eso, representan un tema aún discutible en la
medicina tarahumara. Sin embargo, hay acuerdo en que sólamente pueden
usarlas los especialistas y que siempre están asociadas con rituales.
Las plantas medicinales las recogen en lugares específicos, algunas de
las cuales germinan en campos de cultivo como antropógenas anuales, y
algunas perennes que nosotros consideraríamos maleza. Otras crecen le-
jos de los sitios de habitación y requieren de viajes específicamente
para su recolección.

Los rituales y las curaciones se centran en la figura del chamán
("oueruame"), quien es sacerdote, curandero y especialista en lo sobre-
natural. Aquellos chamanes más reconocidos generalmente han sido entre-
nados en la aldea de Nararachic, donde podría decirse que existe una especie de "seminario". Estos cumplen tres funciones que son: 1- la cu-
ración de enfermedades; 2- supervisión de acontecimientos rituales; y 3-
suministrar, conservar y administrar el uso de peyote. Ahora bien, hay
varios niveles de chamanes que difieren en el papel que desempeñan y en
el prestigio con que cuentan. La categoría más elevada la ocupan aquellos que han logrado varias curaciones exitosas y pronosticado desgra-
cias que afectan a la comunidad. Hay otros practicantes que normalmente
sirven de asistentes al chamán principal. También están los herbola-
rios, quienes se caracterizan por conocer las propiedades curativas de
las hierbas y plantas medicinales. Aparte de estos están los cantores,
quienes no poseen propiedades especiales sino que, mediante la entona-
ción de cantos, ayudan al chamán en sus sesiones curativas.

Para llegar a ocupar la posición de chamán se requiere un largo en-
trenamiento. Casi siempre son tres años y, generalmente, es una activi-
dad que viene por línea familiar. Una vez que el chamán experimentado
dé su aprobación al nuevo practicante, éste entra a servir a la comunidad, no sin antes demostrar sus habilidades.

Es bien interesante observar el sincretismo religioso que ha ocu-
rrido entre las creencias originales de los tarahumara y los diversos
valores del cristianismo. En ocasiones, el chamán se cuelga al cuello
un rosario con un crucifijo y, luego de impartir la señal de la cruz sobre el paciente, le introduce el crucifijo en la boca y sopla. También
es común la erección de cruces en lugares donde se llevarán a cabo ritos
chamanísticos. Aun cuando se han adoptado diversos símbolos de la reli-
gion cristiana, su ideología no ha calado profundamente en el pensa-
miento religioso tarahumara.

El peyote es un halucinógeno muy especial que solamente pueden administrar ciertos chamanes. Se emplea en ocasiones cuando todos los demás esfuerzos han resultado inútiles para curar a un individuo. Los chamanes tarahumara también se ocupan de otras funciones, aparte de curar enfermos, y algunas de ellas incluyen producir lluvias, evitar desastres naturales y presidir las ceremonias de nacimiento. En términos generales, las características son muy similares a las que se pueden observar en algunos lugares de Norteamérica.

BIBLIOGRAFÍA

El-Najjar, Mahmoud Y., and Thomas M. J. Mulinski
    1980   Mummies and Mummification Practices in the Southwestern and Southern United States. In: A. Cockburn and E. Cockburn, eds., Mummies, Disease, and Ancient Cultures, pp. 103-117. Cambridge: Cambridge University Press.

Zingg, Robert M.
    1940   Report on Archaeology of Southern Chihuahua. Contributions of the University of Denver, Center of Latin American Studies, No. 1. Denver, Colorado: The University of Denver.

AUTHORS

ELIZABETH S. DYER ALCAUSKAS, M.A., Anthropology, San Diego State University, formerly held the position of Physical Anthropology Laboratory Technician at the San Diego Museum of Man. Presently, she is Instructor of Anthropology at Palomar Community College in San Marcos, California. Her major interests include osteology and paleopathology.

ROBERT A. BYE, Jr., holds a Ph.D. in Biology from Harvard University. At present, he is Associate Professor of Environmental, Population and Organismic Biology at the University of Colorado, Boulder; Associate Curator of Botany at the Herbarium of the University of Colorado Museum; and *Investigador, Jardín Botánico, Instituto de Biología, Universidad Nacional Autónoma de México*. His major interests include economic and floristic studies of plants of the Sierra Madre Occidental, Mexico, and ethnobotany, ethnoecology, and genetic resource conservation of useful plants of Mexico.

NELLY CANEDO, M.A., Anthropology, University of Toronto, Canada, previously studied biology at San Augustine University in Arequipa, Peru. She worked as a volunteer in the Physical Anthropology Laboratory at the San Diego Museum of Man from 1980 to 1981. Recently, she began her own business in the importation of Peruvian folk art to the United States. Her major interests include the influences of nutritional and vitamin deficiencies on health and disease.

JORGE FELIPE CÁRDENAS holds a B.A. in Anthropology from the University of the Andes, Bogota, Colombia. He is a graduate student in Anthropology at San Diego State University and a volunteer in the Physical Anthropology Laboratory at the San Diego Museum of Man. His previous research includes archaeological investigations of several sites in South America and a spatial analysis of Machu Picchu, Peru. His major interests include osteology and dental health of prehistoric Peruvians.

JUDITH STRUPP GREEN, M.A., Anthropology, Tulane University, was Curator of Latin American Collections at the San Diego Museum of Man from 1962 to 1970. Presently, she is Program Manager of Information Services for the City of San Diego. Her major interests include archaeological and ethnographic folk arts.

SARA B. LAUGHLIN holds an M.S. in Biobehavioral Sciences from the University of Connecticut, Storrs, where she conducted research in the Laboratory of Biological Anthropology. At present, she is a Nutritional Counselor for Bay Kimball Hospital, Putnam, Connecticut. Her major interests include bone biology and human nutrition.

ANNE MARIE LUIBEL-HULEN, B.A., Anthropology, San Diego State University, was a graduate student in the Department of Anthropology, Arizona State University. Presently, she is a Laboratory Technician for United Blood Systems of Arizona, working on histo-compatibility testing and chromosome analysis of Pima Indian populations. She has been accepted into the School of Nursing, Mesa Community College, Mesa, Arizona. Her major interests include health care and population genetics.

STEPHEN A. MILLER, Ph.D., Physics, University of California, Berkeley, is a Physicist at the Naval Ocean Systems Center, San Diego. He has been a volunteer photographer at the San Diego Museum of Man on several projects involving paleopathology. His major interests include Hopi Kachina ceremonies and the uses of native plants by the Indians of the Southwest.

DONALD PATE holds a B.A. in Anthropology from San Diego State University and an M.A. in Anthropology from Brown University and is presently a doctoral candidate at Brown and Harvard Universities. Recently, he was Research Director of the paleodietary and paleoecological aspects of a cemetery site on the lower Murray River in South Australia. His major interests include paleonutrition and paleodiet.

STEPHANIE A. PINTER holds a B.A. in Art History from the University of California, San Diego. She was a volunteer in the Physical Anthropology Laboratory at the San Diego Museum of Man from 1977 to 1981. Currently, she is a doctoral candidate at the University of Pennsylvania and Physical Anthropologist for the excavation of an historic cemetery site in Philadelphia. Her major interests include human growth and development, osteology, and faunal analysis.

SPENCER L. ROGERS holds a Ph.D. in Anthropology from the University of Southern California. He is Professor Emeritus in Anthropology, San Diego State University, and former Scientific Director of the San Diego Museum of Man. Presently, he is Research Anthropologist at the San Diego Museum of Man. His major interests include osteology, forensic anthropology, and medical ethnography.

DAVID D. THOMPSON holds a Ph.D. in Biological Anthropology from the University of Connecticut, Storrs, where he formerly was Assistant Professor in Residence, Department of Behavioral Sciences. Presently, he is a Researcher in the Department of Bone Biology and Osteoporosis, Merck Sharp & Dohme Research Laboratories, West Point, Pennsylvania. His major interests include bone biology, aging, and human variation.

ROSE A. TYSON, M.A., Anthropology, San Diego State University, is Curator of Physical Anthropology at the San Diego Museum of Man. She has participated in osteological fieldwork on the Peruvian north coast at Pacatnamu, and worked in conserving the Hrdlička Paleopathology Collection at the San Diego Museum of Man. Her major interests include osteology, paleopathology, and Baja California prehistory.

BARTON A. WRIGHT, M.A., Anthroplolgy, University of Arizona, was formerly Curator of Anthropology at the Museum of Northern Arizona, Flagstaff, and Scientific Director of the San Diego Museum of Man. Presently, he is a free-lance author, artist, and ethnologist. His major interests include Hopi ethnology and Southwestern arts and crafts.